An Outline of

Chemical Genetics

Bernard S. Strauss, Ph.D.

ASSOCIATE PROFESSOR OF MICROBIOLOGY
THE UNIVERSITY OF CHICAGO

W. B. Saunders Company

PHILADELPHIA & LONDON   1960

Library of Congress Catalog Card Number: 60–13689

"I ca'n't believe *that!*" said Alice.

"Ca'n't you?" the Queen said in a pitying tone. "Try again: draw a long breath, and shut your eyes."

Alice laughed. "There's no use trying," she said: "One *ca'n't* believe impossible things."

"I daresay you haven't had much practice," said the Queen. "When I was your age, I always did it for half-an-hour a day. Why, sometimes I've believed as many as six impossible things before breakfast. . . ."

from Through the Looking-Glass
by Lewis Carroll

Preface

This book is designed for readers who have heard some of the facts of modern genetics, particularly those relating to the startling developments in the study of the nucleic acids, but who have not had the opportunity to see how these developments affect genetic theory as a whole. It is the outgrowth of a series of lectures delivered to graduate students in the Faculty of Medicine at Osaka University. The audience consisted mainly of people with biochemical training and interests rather than of professional geneticists. I have, therefore, assumed some knowledge of chemistry, but only a brief encounter with the Mendelian laws, and have felt it necessary to include some material on the basic principles of genetics. In addition, I have had in mind my friends in the various scientific disciplines who have heard snatches of the recent developments in genetics and find them fascinating but who have not yet been persuaded to study the detailed literature. It is my belief that genetics will benefit if such persons can read a more complete account of the present status of chemical genetics than is now available. Ideally such an account should be short enough to permit consecutive reading and detailed enough to include the important facts.

PREFACE

I have attempted to give as complete an account of the chemical nature and behavior of the hereditary unit as is possible in a short space. The treatment is selective, subjective and purposely naive. The simplest interpretation of the relation between genes and enzymes has been adopted, for example, because of its heuristic value and because of its logical appeal and in spite of the possible dangers of the approach. The test of the unified picture I have attempted will be its appearance in the light of the discoveries that will be made, probably before these lectures are finally printed.

I would like to take this opportunity to thank Professor Hideo Kikkawa who suggested that I might give these lectures and in whose laboratory at Osaka I spent a stimulating year. My thanks are also due to the Fulbright Commission, the Guggenheim Foundation and the Trustees of Syracuse University, all of whom helped make the year in Japan possible. Finally, I must thank the students at both Osaka University and at Kanazawa University for their patience in listening to me speak in a foreign tongue.

BERNARD S. STRAUSS

Contents

CONTENTS

CONTENTS

CONTENTS

Introductory Statement

This book discusses the following ideas which form a conceptual scheme for present day chemical genetics:

1. The genetic determinants of organisms are particulate in nature and occur linked together in linear fashion. Occasionally changes in the linkage relationships may occur during, or closely following, the time of the duplication of the genetic material. Such *recombination* of genetic characteristics constitutes the basic fact of genetics as a separate science.

2. The genetic information is carried from generation to generation by a chemical substance—deoxyribonucleic acid (DNA). This substance is a polymer built of four nucleotides arranged to form a double helix. The helix is so arranged that each strand is an exact *complement* of the other. The genetic information is coded in the DNA so that the sequence in which the four nucleotides occur constitutes an "alphabet" which spells out the genetic information.

3. The genetic material acts by controlling the formation of proteins. Genes not only control the quantitative presence or absence of particular proteins but they also determine the qualitative properties of the proteins which are formed. This control of protein characteristics occurs by genetic control of the sequence of amino acids in the protein polypeptide chains. The code of nucleotides determines the sequence of the amino acids, and changes in the sequence of nucleotides are reflected by changes in the sequence of amino acids in the corresponding protein.

4. Occasional errors in the duplication of the nucleotide code

may occur at the time of gene reproduction. Such errors, if functional, lead to the production of altered gene products (proteins) and are therefore recognized as mutations.

This conceptual scheme accounts for most of the observations made in the study of chemical genetics. There are certain observations which do not fit and there are certain areas of almost complete ignorance. There is no evidence that permits decision as to *how* DNA (the genetic substance) controls protein formation since there is no experiment which demonstrates a specific metabolic role for DNA. There is still no real information as to how DNA reproduces at the biological level; there is no really complete explanation of the genetic fact of recombination, and there is little real evidence as to how mutations originate. Recent evidence, obtained with microorganisms, which suggests that a strand of DNA in the process of duplication may select which portion of two parental chains will be copied only makes the problem more difficult. It is becoming extremely difficult to distinguish between genetic recombination and mutation. Even our ideas about the structure of the genetic material may, eventually, be changed since a virus DNA structure containing only one polynucleotide strand in the helix has been described. It is therefore a good idea to examine the basis of the conceptual ideas that now serve as a guide for so much work in the very active field of chemical genetics.

Chapter One

The Genetic Control of Protein Synthesis

"Biochemical genetics is a field cultivated more by the biologist than by the biochemist. The biologist has been insistently pushed in this direction by advances in genetics while the biochemist has so far found nothing in his subject that tends so to urge him. History might well have been otherwise for as this review attempts to make clear, genes are as much a part of biochemistry as chemistry is of inheritance."

G. W. Beadle

I. Biochemical Genetics

Alkaptonuria is a disease in which large amounts of the substance homogentisic acid, 2,5 dihydroxyphenylacetic acid, are excreted in the urine throughout life (Knox 1958). In the first decade of this century Garrod's investigation of this condition led him to conclude that it was an "inborn error of metabolism" with a congenital basis. By the 1930's it was clearly established that patients suffering from the disease carried two doses of a mutant gene and that in most cases persons carrying one mutant and one normal genetic factor (heterozygotes) were normal in their physiology. The disease therefore is the result of a single Mendelian recessive gene. Garrod recognized that the excretion of homogentisic acid represented the result of a block in a normal series of reactions and that the excreted substance was a metabolic intermediate which could not be further metabolized because of the genetic deficiency (Garrod 1902, 1909).

Garrod worked at a time when geneticists were just establishing their science and when the idea of a sequence of metabolic reactions was new to biochemistry. Although he collected other examples of hereditary metabolic defects in man and although his work was not forgotten, it did not really influence the development of genetics.

It was not until Beadle and Tatum showed in 1941 that gene mutation in the mold Neurospora resulted in the inactivation of particular metabolic reactions, with the consequent development of nutritional requirements, that most biologists paid very much attention to the connection between genetics and biochemistry.

During the period immediately preceding the work of Beadle and Tatum a number of studies had indicated that the genes might act by controlling the reactions of intermediate metabolism. Studies on the inheritance of flower color and of eye color in various insects made it seem likely that genes acted by controlling single biochemical reactions. I am not certain of the historical accuracy with which the chain of events leading to the experiment performed by G. W. Beadle and E. L. Tatum is recorded since much of the record is definitely hearsay, although Beadle has recorded a part of it in his Nobel Lecture (1959). Beadle and Tatum working at Stanford University were attempting to isolate and study one of the soluble "hormones" involved in the production of Drosophila eye color but became discouraged at the problem of avoiding microbial alterations in the necessarily complex medium used for the fruit fly. They reasoned that if genes controlled metabolic reactions it should be possible to increase the nutritional requirements of an organism by gene mutation. Mutation, inactivating a gene, might lead to the cessation of the synthesis of a required substance which would then have to be supplied as an additional nutritional supplement in the medium.

The choice of Neurospora as the organism to be used can be seen, in retrospect anyhow, to have been more than a matter of pure chance. The Neurospora life cycle had been worked out by B. O. Dodge in the 1920's.

Neurospora crassa is an ascomycete; that means it is a fungus whose sexual spores are produced in a sack or ascus. Its vegetative growth is similar to that of most filamentous fungi; many filaments or hyphae associate to form a mycelium and there are multinucleate, asexual spores called conidia produced at the end of specialized hyphae. Sexual reproduction does occur, there are two mating types, A and a, and the sexual spores are formed in groups of eight in an ascus. Many asci are located in the fruiting body or perithecium. The sexual spores, or ascospores, are resistant to environmental conditions and germinate only when heated to 60° C for about half an hour or when activated with certain chemical agents like furfural. The Neurospora life cycle had not been completely worked out in the laboratory until Dodge, or an assistant, inadvertently placed some plates in an oven instead of an incubator and then avoided discarding the plates long enough after their removal from the oven for the spores to germinate and produce a thriving culture.

The Neurospora ascospores are genetically haploid, as are the nuclei in the conidia and the vegetative mycelium. This means that there are no problems of dominance (Chapter 3); there is only one dose of each gene in any nucleus and any mutant characteristic will be expressed unless the genetic background contains special modifier or suppressor genes. It is therefore possible to recognize mutations produced by a treatment more immediately than with diploid organisms such as Drosophila since only one dose of the mutant factor is required instead of the two required for most (recessive) factors in Drosophila.

At a seminar given at Cornell University while Beadle was a graduate student, Dodge pointed out some results on the segregation of mating type in Neurospora which were recognized by Beadle and by other students present as evidence for a particular genetic phenomenon called "four strand crossing over" which will be discussed later. According to the story as told by Beadle, Dodge later went to T. H. Morgan, the great Drosophila geneticist, to try to convince him that Neurospora was much better material for genetic studies than Drosophila! Apparently Dodge did convince Morgan at least to accept a culture of Neurospora and when Morgan moved to the California Institute of Technology he carried the culture with him. According to the story (as it was told to graduate students) C. C. Lindegren arrived at Caltech soon afterwards and was handed the culture by Morgan with instructions to do something with it. The result was a series of excellent studies on the genetics of Neurospora. Coincidentally Beadle was a post-doctoral fellow at Caltech.

Neurospora will grow on a very simple medium but until 1941 the details of a synthetic medium had not been worked out. In that year W. J. Robbins demonstrated that Neurospora would grow on a medium containing inorganic salts, sugar and the vitamin, biotin ("minimal medium"). It therefore became possible to study the growth of Neurospora in a chemically defined medium. Beadle and Tatum's experiment was then done as follows: asexual spores, or conidia, of the mold Neurospora were irradiated with X-rays and the treated spores were used to fertilize non-irradiated material of the opposite mating type. The sexual spores produced were then isolated and germinated on a complete medium which contained a variety of growth factors. The cultures originating from single sexual spores were tested one by one for their ability to grow on the original or minimal medium. Strains that would not grow on minimal medium but which would grow on the complete medium were tested for their response to a series of vitamins, amino acids and purines and pyrimidines until some supplement that permitted growth when added to the minimal medium was found. The mutant strain was then crossed to a wild type, or normal strain, to determine the genetic basis of the mutation (Chapter 3).

As a result of this and successive experiments a large number of mutants were isolated, most of which required the addition of only a single supplement added to the minimal medium in order to mimic growth of the normal strain. In addition it turned out that in those cases in which normal growth was restored by a single supplement only a single Mendelian gene was affected by the mutagenic treatment.

The very fact that mutants could be isolated requiring definite chemical substances important in metabolism and that these mutants differed from the wild type by only a single Mendelian factor was itself an important fact since it clearly demonstrated that the ordinary reactions of metabolism were under genetic control. It had previously seemed quite plausible that these reactions, representing the continuing reactions of the cell, might be propagated independently of the genes, but the mass of evidence obtained after the original experiment of Beadle and Tatum showed the closeness of the relationship between genes and metabolism.

This experiment was the beginning of a series of investigations on the relationship between genetics and metabolism, partly because it was now possible to produce mutants of the desired biochemical type instead of waiting for them to occur by chance. Over the years the efficiency with which mutants may be selected has been greatly improved. One technique developed by Woodward *et al.* (1954) is useful with Neurospora and other filamentous fungi and is based on the fact that certain types of mutant spores do not germinate in minimal medium in contrast to the wild types which produce hyphae, or germ tubes, within a few hours. Suspensions of spores are treated with a mutagenic agent and incubated with agitation in a minimal medium. At intervals the suspension is filtered through gauze. The germinated wild type spores are captured by the gauze while the mutants pass through and can later be plated on a selective medium and isolated.

An extremely useful technique developed by Davis (1948) and separately by Lederberg and Zinder (1948) for use with bacteria is based on the fact that penicillin kills only growing cells. Bacteria are treated with a mutagenic agent, passed through an intermediate growth phase (as discussed in Chapter 4 most mutations are not expressed without this period of growth) and then subjected to the action of penicillin in minimal medium. The wild type cells are killed, the mutants survive. The antibiotic is removed by washing the cells or by the action of the enzyme penicillinase and the remaining cells are plated on medium supplemented with the desired growth factor.

Other techniques are available. The "Starvation Technique" developed by Fries, Pontecorvo (1953) and applied to Neurospora by Lester and Gross (1959) depends on the fact that certain double mutants (strains with two independent growth requirements as a result of distinct mutations) survive incubation in minimal medium more successfully than do strains with only single requirements. The strains with single requirements tend to die off in some cases by a kind of "unbalanced growth." Incubation in minimal medium therefore enriches the proportion of new (double) mutants.

Another deceptively simple technique was developed by the Lederbergs (1952). Colonies of a microorganism are developed on a suitable complete medium and are then transferred *en masse* to plates of different types by the use of a velvet stamp. The stamp is pressed to the surface of the original plate and then a number of

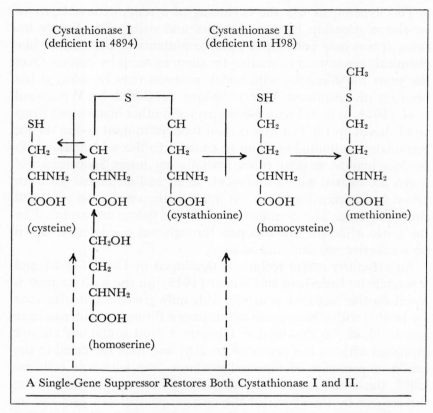

Figure 1. Action of the suppressors of the homocysteine-requiring mutants of Neurospora. Data of Giles (1951) and Fischer (1957).

replicas can be stamped out by pressing the velvet to a fresh agar surface. Mutants are recognized by comparison of the replica plates with the original; mutant strains will not grow on certain of the replica plates. This replica plating method is important because no selective agent is used to screen out the majority of wild types. The possibility that the method of selection used may yield mutants of a specific type is one of the specters that can confuse the interpretation of experiments using induced mutations.

Some of the characteristics of the "biochemical" or nutritionally deficient mutants are easily illustrated by a consideration of the methionine-requiring mutants of Neurospora. Mutants of this type are obtained in high frequency by most of the mutation selection methods. It can be shown that the mutation of several different genes can lead to strains that will grow only when methionine is added to the minimal medium. Several mutant classes can be separated. One class grows only on the addition of methionine; a second class will grow when minimal medium is supplemented with either methionine or with homocysteine, while a third class will grow when supplementation is with either methionine, homocysteine or with cystathionine (Fig. 1). Mutants of the second class, those that will respond to either methionine or to homocysteine but not to cystathionine, *accumulate* cystathionine in the mycelium. In addition the enzyme which splits cystathionine to form homocysteine and which is easily demonstrated in the wild type cannot be demonstrated with extracts of these mutants (Fischer 1957). Patterns of this type have been recognized with other mutant types and have given rise to the concept of the *Genetic Block*: As a result of gene mutation an enzyme activity is diminished or eliminated; and as a result of the loss of this enzyme activity an intermediate may accumulate, be excreted, or be converted in quantity to some derivative; finally, the end product of the particular chain of biochemical reactions will not be produced and may have to be supplied in the diet. The concept of the genetic block is independent of the mechanism by which the enzyme activity is altered; enzymes may be lost, or altered, or their activity may be inhibited by extraneous substances (Wagner and Mitchell 1955).

The accumulation of intermediates and the development of nutritional requirements that may be satisfied by end products or by the proper intermediates are properties that have been used for the identification of pathways of metabolism. Information obtained with "biochemical mutants" has been useful in determining the pathway of synthesis of many of the amino acids and of some of the vitamins and purines and pyrimidines (De Busk 1956). From the point of view of genetics, however, it is more important to inquire as to the mechanism by which enzyme activities are lowered or eliminated.

II. Genes and Protein Structure

It was assumed by Beadle and by many others that the genetic control of metabolic reactions was exerted by a control over enzyme production or structure. There is no doubt that genetic change does lead to a change in enzyme activity in a variety of organisms (Table 1. A complete list has been compiled by Fincham 1959).

9

TABLE 1.   *Some Enzymes Shown To Be under Genetic Control*

ENZYME	ORGANISM	REACTION
1. Galactose-1-phosphate transuridylase	Man	Galactose-1-phosphate + UDPG → Glucose-1-phosphate + UDPGalactose
2. Xanthine dehydrogenase	Drosophila	(a) 2-amino-4-hydroxypteridine → isoxanthopterin (b) Hypoxanthine → Xanthine → Uric acid
3. Tyrosinase	Neurospora	Tyrosine → Melanin
4. Glutamic dehydrogenase	Neurospora	α ketoglutaric acid + DPNH + H^+ + NH_3 ⟶ Glutamic acid + DPN^+
5. Adenylsuccinase	Neurospora	(a) Adenylsuccinic acid → Fumaric acid + adenosine 5′ phosphate (b) 5-amino-4-imidazole-(N succinylo-carboxamide) Ribotide → 5-amino-4-imidazole carboxamide Ribotide + Fumaric acid
6. Tryptophan synthetase	Neurospora (*E. coli*)	Indole glycerol phosphate + serine → Tryptophan + triose phosphate
7. Dihydroxy acid dehydrase	Neurospora	(a) α, β dihydroxy β ethyl butyric acid → α keto β methyl valeric acid (b) α, β dihydroxy β methyl butyric acid → α keto isovaleric acid

In all the cases listed in Table 1 there is evidence that the enzyme deficiency segregates as though it were controlled by a genetic factor in the Mendelian sense and there is no reason to suppose that the production of an inhibitor is responsible for the loss of activity. The problem therefore becomes "how does gene change result in a change in enzyme activity?" but an answer to this question requires digression into the realm of studies on protein structure.

It is an interesting and perhaps significant coincidence that the Nobel prize in chemistry was awarded to Sanger for determination of the amino acid sequence of insulin in the same year that Beadle and Tatum and Lederberg received the prize in medicine for their work in microbial genetics. Sanger utilized the fact that dinitrofluorobenzene will react with free amino groups to form dinitrophenyl derivatives that are stable to the hydrolytic conditions that result in the splitting of the peptide bond. The derivatives have the advantage of being colored and are separated without too much difficulty by paper chromatography.

Proteins are essentially polypeptides in which both the amino and carboxyl groups of the amino acids are combined in peptide bonds with the exception of those groups at the ends of the chains and on the defunctional amino acids such as lysine or glutamic acid. Treatment of a protein with dinitrofluorobenzene followed by hydrolysis permits recognition of the amino acids at the terminal end of the proteins since only these can form colored dinitrophenyl derivatives. Subsequent partial hydrolysis of the protein produces peptides of various sizes. Knowing the component at one end it is possible to piece together the sequence of the amino acids in large peptides by the overlapping obtained when smaller peptides are analyzed (Fig. 2). The essential part of this method is the recognition of the end of the peptide chain by the method of "end group analysis" using dinitrofluorobenzene and similar compounds.

As a result of a series of painstaking investigations Sanger was able to establish the sequence of amino acids in the insulin molecule (Sanger and Thompson 1953). Quite apart from the importance of this achievement for the study of the function of this important protein hormone is its theoretical significance for the structure of proteins as a whole. There was some doubt expressed that a collection of protein molecules might represent duplications of the same molecule in the same sense that a pure sample of benzoic acid represents a collection of identical molecules. Since pro-

---

A. The following dipeptides were obtained by partial hydrolysis:

  Ileu-val   Glu-cys

    Val-glu

    Glu-glu

B. The following larger peptides were obtained:

  Ileu-val-glu   Cys-cys-ala

 Gly-ileu-val-glu

     Glu-cys–cys–ala

 Ileu-val-glu-glu

C. Therefore the sequence must be:

  Gly-ileu-val-glu-glu-cys-cys-ala

Figure 2. The elucidation of peptide sequences. Identification of the sequence in an octapeptide. (After Fruton and Simmonds, 1958.)

11

beef	Cys - Cys - Ala - Ser - Val - Cys - . . .
pig	Cys - Cys - Thr - Ser - Ileu - Cys - . . .
sheep	Cys - Cys - Ala - Gly - Val - Cys - . . .
horse	Cys - Cys - Thr - Gly - Ileu - Cys - . . .
whale	Cys - Cys - Thr - Ser - Ileu - Cys - . . .

Figure 3. Amino acid sequences in a portion of the polypeptide chain of insulin obtained from different species. (After Ycas 1958 from data of Harris, Sanger and Naughton 1956.)

tein molecules are so large a good case might be made for their "micro-heterogeneity"; that is, small differences between molecules of the same protein might occur (Colvin, Smith and Cook 1954). Sanger's feat established that there was a definite, *unique* sequence of amino acids in the insulin molecule. At the polypeptide level therefore a protein must be considered as a definite chemical compound in the sense implied by chemists since Lavoisier. An additional fact, of great potential interest to geneticists, emerged from these studies. The amino acid sequence of insulins obtained from different species is essentially identical but there are a few differences (Fig. 3). At one portion of the polypeptide chains there tends to be a substitution of particular amino acids at particular positions. For example glycine in sheep substitutes for serine in cattle at one particular position; isoleucine in the pig may substitute for valine in cattle at another position (Harris, Sanger and Naughton 1956). These results suggest that species differences are reflected by amino acid substitutions in protein molecules. If we assume that the differences between species are genetic in nature, then the difference in the amino acid sequences must be genetically controlled and the hypothesis that genes control protein structure by control of amino acid sequence in the polypeptide chain is suggested.

The best evidence for this hypothesis comes from studies on the abnormal hemoglobins produced in certain congenital anemias, particularly in the condition of sickle cell anemia. In sickle cell anemia the erythrocytes form a sickle shaped structure when subjected to low oxygen tensions, in contrast to the behavior of normal blood cells. Pauling, Itano and their co-workers (1949) showed that sickle cell anemia is "A Molecular Disease" (to use Pauling's very graphic term) since the disease is a result of the production of an altered hemoglobin, one with electrophoretic and solubility properties different from normal hemoglobin. The disease is the result of a single, recessive Mendelian gene; gene change has therefore resulted in the production of large quantities of an altered protein.

Although the complete amino acid sequence of hemoglobin has not been determined, it is possible to split both the normal and sickle cell hemoglobin into peptides and then to compare the identity of the peptides produced. Ingram (1956) has shown that the two hemoglobins differ only in the structure of one of the peptides (Fig. 4). Determination of the sequence of amino acids in this peptide showed further that the difference results from the substitution of a single valine residue for a glutamic acid residue present in normal hemoglobin. Hemoglobin from individuals suffering from hemoglobin-C disease substitutes a lysine residue for glutamic acid at the same position in the peptide (Hunt and Ingram 1958). There is evidence that the sickle cell anemia and the hemoglobin-C disease factors are *allelic,* that is changed forms of the same gene, and these determinations therefore show that gene change can result in a change in amino acid sequence in a particular protein. It is therefore reasonable to suppose that at least one mechanism of gene action is by control of the amino acid sequence of proteins. (It is only an inference to suppose that this is the only mechanism for gene action.) The different physical properties of the hemoglobin from diseased individuals are also accounted for by these findings since the substitution of an uncharged

$$\text{HbA} \ldots \ldots \overset{+}{\text{Val}} - \overset{+}{\text{His}} - \text{Leu} - \text{Thr} - \text{Pro} - \overset{-}{Glu} - \overset{-}{\text{Glu}} - \overset{+}{\text{Lys}}^{-} \ldots \ldots$$

$$\text{HbS} \ldots \ldots \overset{+}{\text{Val}} - \overset{+}{\text{His}} - \text{Leu} - \text{Thr} - \text{Pro} - Val - \overset{-}{\text{Glu}} - \overset{+}{\text{Lys}}^{-} \ldots \ldots$$

$$\text{HbC} \ldots \ldots \overset{+}{\text{Val}} - \overset{+}{\text{His}} - \text{Leu} - \text{Thr} - \text{Pro} - \overset{+}{Lys} - \overset{-}{\text{Glu}} - \overset{+}{\text{Lys}}^{-} \ldots \ldots$$

HbA = normal human hemoglobin
HbS = sickle cell anemia hemoglobin
HbC = hemoglobin-C disease hemoglobin

Figure 4. Sequence of amino acid residues in a segment of one of the polypeptide chains of hemoglogin. (After Perutz 1958 and personal communication.)

or positively charged residue for the negatively charged glutamyl residue in the peptide would be expected to change the electrophoretic and solubility properties of the substituted protein.

There is good evidence, discussed in detail in the next chapter, that the genetic information is contained within the structure of a chemical substance, deoxyribonucleic acid (DNA). DNA is a large linear polymer constructed of four different nucleotides and these nucleotides appear to occur at random throughout the structure of the DNA molecule. If the genetic material determines the sequence of amino acids in peptides and if DNA is the genetic material, then there should be some correspondence between the sequence of nucleotides in DNA (the genetic material) and the sequence of amino acids in the polypeptide chains controlled by the genes (Crick 1958). The nucleotide sequence can be considered a kind of code or alphabet preserving a message to the cell which tells it what types of protein to make.

Attempts to discover satisfactory codes have been made. The problem, of course, is to determine how four elements are combined to uniquely determine the twenty amino acids while also indicating "stops" between proteins and between amino acids so that the cell reads the information for one protein without confusing it with a second. The most promising attempts suggest a code in which a "triplet" of three nucleotides determines each amino acid. It is my impression that no perfectly satisfactory code has been worked out as yet but the ideas and the approach are stimulating (Ycas 1958).

It might be assumed that the genetic material would act by controlling those parts of the protein enzymes which combine with the substrate molecules but this is not necessarily true. The insulins from different species show *no* functional differentiation in spite of their different amino acid content and the hemoglobin from normal and sickle cell anemias has the same oxygen dissociation curve (determined under non-physiological conditions). It even appears that the "active centers" or combining sites of a range of diverse enzymes may have a common amino acid sequence; their specificity of sequence may reside in other parts of the molecule. It does appear that the enzymes thrombin, chymotrypsin, trypsin and phosphoglucomutase all have the common amino acid sequence glycine—aspartic acid—serine—glycine—glutamic acid—alanine as part of their active sites (Gladner and Laki 1958).

14

III. *Qualitative Changes in Enzyme Structure*

The experiments with sickle cell hemoglobin make it seem likely that gene change should result in the production of protein enzymes with characteristics differing qualitatively from the normal enzyme. Such enzymes have been found but in general the change is not reflected by a change in the kinetic constants (Michaelis constant, etc.,) which would reflect changes at the combining site, but rather by changes in the activation energy or heat stability of the enzyme protein. Under certain growth conditions Neurospora will produce tyrosinase, the enzyme oxidizing the aromatic amino acid tyrosine to produce the biological pigment, melanin. Two wild type strains of Neurospora have been found each of which produces a tyrosinase with different thermostability; one enzyme is relatively stable to short heat treatments, the other loses its catalytic activity (Fig. 5). Both enzymes catalyze the same reaction(s) with essentially the same kinetic constants—only the thermostabilities are different. The two enzymes are determined by allelic genes. Crosses of thermostable by thermolabile invariably yield equal numbers of both types in the progeny, the result to be expected in this haploid organism if the difference were de-

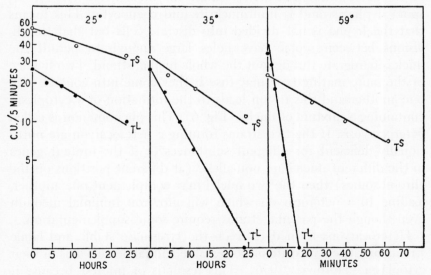

Figure 5. Stability of tyrosinase enzyme activity in two strains of Neurospora differing by a single gene. Ordinate: Residual activity in colorimeter units per five minutes plotted on a log scale. Abscissae: Time of exposure to the indicated temperature. (Horowitz and Fling, Genetics, vol. 38, 1953.)

15

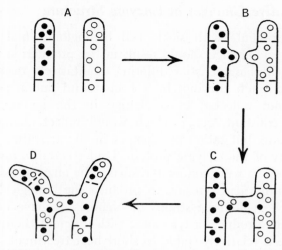

Figure 6. Heterocaryosis in Neurospora. Closed circles represent nuclei of one strain, open circles represent nuclei of the other. The figure is very diagrammatic.

termined by alternate forms of a single genetic factor (Horowitz and Fling 1953).

The biology of Neurospora permits another type of experiment on the determination of the tyrosinase enzyme activity. The Neurospora hyphal strand is multinucleate and coenocytic. This means that the hypha is not divided into discrete cells but that the divisions between septae have holes large enough to permit the nuclei to migrate throughout the whole hyphal strand. Two hyphae of the same mating type may fuse if they come into contact with one another and this fusion leads to the formation of a cytoplasm containing a mixture of nuclei (Fig. 6). This phenomenon is called *heterocaryosis*. If the two strains forming a heterocaryon are nutritionally deficient for different substances or if the mutant genes in the different nuclei are non-allelic (at different positions on the chromosomes) then the two nuclei may complement one another, leading to a heterocaryon which will grow on minimal medium even though the parental strains require some supplementation.

Heterocaryons formed between the tyrosinase stable and labile strains produce a mixture of both stable and labile enzymes in their cytoplasm (Horowitz 1956). This result is of interest because it indicates a lack of gene interaction similar to that shown by certain heterozygotes of true diploid organisms. Heterocaryons mimic the diploid condition of higher organisms since two alleles of a single gene may be present in one cytoplasm. It is therefore possible to study problems of dominance by the use of heterocaryons. (In the heterocaryons it is necessary to know the ratio in which both types of nuclei occur, and this varies instead of being always 1:1 as in heterozygotes.) Apparently there is no dominance in the case of tyrosinase production just as there is no dominance in the production of the different forms of hemoglobin. The heterozygote for sickle cell anemia displays no symptoms of the disease but does have what is known as sickle cell trait. Erythrocytes from heterozygotes will sickle and these erythrocytes contain from 54 to 78 per cent of normal and 22 to 46 per cent of sickle cell hemoglobin (see Chapter 6). Results of this type obtained with widely different types of organisms indicate that the effect of the genes on protein formation is determined by the dosage of genes present and, in some cases at any rate, may be independent of any sort of interaction between the different alleles.

If the tip of a heterocaryotic Neurospora mycelium is cut off with the aid of a glass needle and the hyphal tip is transferred to fresh medium it will grow and yield a new mycelium if the original hyphal tip contains at least one nucleus. If the tip contains only one nucleus or contains two or more nuclei of the same type this procedure results in the resolution of the heterocaryon into one of its original components. Resolution of heterocaryons producing a mixture of both types of tyrosinase leads to the isolation of strains which produce only one type of enzyme, characteristic of the nucleus. This type of experiment indicates that enzyme type is determined only by the nucleus even though, as most recent experiments indicate, the enzyme may actually be synthesized in the cytoplasm.

In the case of the tyrosinases of Neurospora or of the hemoglobins of man it is possible to recognize the production of some altered substance by the allele because catalytic activity is not altered by the particular change in protein structure. One may inquire in general whether any substitute product appears if an organism is not able to produce a particular enzyme because of some genetic change. There is no absolute answer to this question but a series of elegant investigations on the tryptophan synthetase system in Neurospora and in the colon bacillus *Escherichia coli* by Bonner, Yanofsky and Suskind do provide some tentative answers.

The tryptophan synthetase system as prepared from *E. coli* participates in the following reactions (Yanofsky 1959) and it is

17

$$\begin{array}{lcl}
\text{Indole + L-serine} & \rightarrow & \text{L-tryptophan} \\
\text{Indoleglycerol phosphate} & \rightleftharpoons & \text{indole + triose phosphate} \\
\text{Indoleglycerol phosphate +} & \rightarrow & \text{L-tryptophan + triose} \\
\text{L-serine} & & \text{phosphate}
\end{array}$$

likely that the same series of reactions is catalyzed by the enzyme obtained from Neurospora. A series of allelic mutants which are unable to carry out the condensation with serine to form tryptophan has been obtained from both organisms. (It is already evident that one of the difficulties in discussing genetic problems is the difficulty in defining exactly what is meant by "the same gene" or by the term "allele." I intend to discuss this problem in detail in the third chapter. In the meantime the term "allele" will mean an alternate form of a particular gene even though an adequate operational definition of "gene" has not been given.) Crosses of the different Neurospora mutants yield no wild types (or at most very few) so that they appear to be changes at the same genetic locus. Nonetheless these mutants differ with respect to their temperature sensitivity, indole accumulation, ability to form material serologically related to tryptophan synthetase and in their suppressibility by non-allelic genes. (A suppressor gene in combination with a second, non-allelic mutant gene yields an organism which behaves more like the wild type than the mutant. The suppressor genes are recognized in Neurospora by the peculiar ratios of mutant to wild type obtained when a suppresssed mutant is crossed to a true wild type, Chapter 4.)

There is evidence that some of the mutant strains can still catalyze the formation of indole from indoleglycerol phosphate although they are unable to form tryptophan. Preparations from the two Neurospora mutants which carry out this conversion require either pyridoxal phosphate or pyridoxal phosphate and serine. Wild-type preparations do not require these cofactors for the conversion of indoleglycerol phosphate to indole (De Moss and Bonner 1959). Mutation has therefore led to an alteration in the characteristics of the enzyme catalysis.

The suppressor mutations which have been obtained have some very peculiar properties but these properties seem to be duplicated by other systems in different organisms; for example, with the suppressors of some of the adenine-requiring mutants of *Aspergillus nidulans* (Pontecorvo 1956). The suppressors of the Neurospora mutants partially restore the ability of these mutants to grow in the absence of added tryptophan and to make enzyme, but the suppressor mutations display a specificity and only permit the formation of tryptophan synthetase when combined with certain of the mutant, *td*, alleles (Yanofsky 1956). For example about 24 different *td* alleles have been studied. A suppressor of *td-2* will not suppress *td-1*, *td-3* or *td-6* (Table 2). Some of the suppressors will suppress two or more *td* alleles and many different suppressor genes can be isolated which will suppress any particular allele. So far no suppressor gene has been found for the *td-1* allele. This specificity of action shows that the *td* alleles are still necessary for the production of the original, non-mutant enzyme activity. Suppressor action here is by means of gene interaction and the mutant *td* alleles are the repositories of the information needed for the production of tryptophan synthetase.

Certain of the *td* alleles produce an antigen which is serologically indistinguishable from tryptophan synthetase although it does not have enzyme activity. This material is termed CRM (cross reacting material) (Suskind 1957). The antibody produced by the injection of purified Neurospora tryptophan synthetase into rabbits has the convenient property of inhibiting enzyme activity. Absorption of antibody with material prepared from *td* mutants results in a loss of inhibitory power indicating the reaction of the antibody with a component of the *td* extract. Only certain alleles produce CRM and these are the alleles which can be suppressed. Strain *td-1* for example, which cannot be suppressed, does not produce the antigen.

All of the results with the *td* mutants can be interpreted by supposing that mutation results in the production of an altered protein which may possess a portion, or none, of the original

TABLE 2.   *Specificity of the Suppressors of the* td *Locus in Neurospora**

TD MUTANT	SUPPRESSOR GENE			
	SU-2	SU-3	SU-6	SU-24
td - 1	—	—	—	—
td - 2	+†	—	+	—
td - 3	—	+	—	+
td - 6	—	—	+	—
td - 24	—	+	—	+

* After Yanofsky and Bonner (1955)

† + indicates that the suppressor gene restores the ability of the *td* mutant to grow in the absence of added tryptophan.

19

catalytic activity. One interpretation of the suppressor action is that the strains which can be suppressed produce a slightly altered enzyme which is inhibited by substances normally present in the organism. Reducing the quantity of inhibitor by any means would result in partial restoration of enzyme activity. This explanation does have the advantage of indicating how several different (non-allelic) suppressor genes might suppress the same *td* locus. In some cases purification of extracts of *td* mutants leads to the appearance of enzyme activity, presumably by removing a naturally occurring inhibitor from the system. The enzyme produced by these mutants is more easily inhibited by certain of the trace metals (*i.e.* zinc ion) than is the normal material (Suskind and Kurek 1959). Only an amino acid sequence study of the purified proteins can give a definitive answer but these studies do support the idea that gene change can lead to small, discrete changes in protein molecules. It is also possible to answer the question asked above; in some cases at least a mutant gene will lead to the production of an altered substance which will be found in the organism even though it may have no normal function.

The studies with the tryptophan synthesizing enzyme and with the Neurospora tyrosinase demonstrate that single Mendelian genes can control the qualitative properties of particular enzyme protein molecules. The idea that genes control protein structure by control over the amino acid sequence of the peptide chains is a reasonable deduction from the results with the aberrant hemo-globins of man. In fact I will propose (Chapter 3) as an ideal (but not yet an operational) definition of the gene "that section of the genetic material involved in the determination of the amino acid sequence of a single polypeptide." This is close to, but not identical with, the idea that single genes control the formation of single enzymes (Beadle 1945).

The close relationship between single gene changes and single nutritional requirements which appeared in the early studies with Neurospora prompted the development of this "one gene—one enzyme" idea. The value of the idea is indicated by its success in interpreting most of the data of chemical genetics and by the ease with which this idea accounts for the phenomenon of changed amino acid sequence in mutant hemoglobin molecules. Nonetheless it is true that changes at more than one genetic locus can affect the activity or the production of a single enzyme. Demonstrations of this sort are now frequent enough that they fail to elicit surprise.

Suppressor genes, as indicated above, are genes which affect the activity of enzymes which appear to be primarily controlled by other genetic loci and many *different* suppressor genes may affect the activity of the same enzyme system. Although a case has been described in which a suppressor gene leads to the production of a protein not present in the unsuppressed mutant strain (Crawford and Yanofsky 1959), in all cases studied so far the suppressor works only in the presence of particular alleles of the mutant gene so that the suppressor must have only a secondary effect on its enzyme.

Several cases have been described in which the change of different genes results in loss of activity of a single enzyme. Glassman and Mitchell (1959) showed that two distinct genes can control the presence of xanthine dehydrogenase in Drosophila. Three distinct mutations cause a loss of nitrate reductase in Neurospora (Silver and McElroy 1954). Several different mutations affect the production of beta galactosidase in *Escherichia coli*. In this system it appears that one genic system (z) controls the ability of the organism to make the enzyme while another distinct but closely linked gene (i) determines the amount of enzyme which is normally formed, apparently by a complex mechanism involving an inhibitor of unknown structure (Pardee, Jacob and Monod 1959). It is evident therefore that several genes can be involved in the production and the determination of the activity of single enzymes. Since apparently single enzyme systems may involve more than one protein (and certainly more than one peptide chain) (Crawford and Yanofsky 1958), these findings do not affect the idea that genes control the sequence of the amino acids in a peptide.

IV. *Partial Genetic Blocks*

Some genes may act by controlling the amount of particular enzymes rather than their qualitative nature. Most of the studies that have been discussed so far are based on a highly selected class of mutants. Often in studies of biochemical genetics only the mutants with "all or none" characteristics are selected for further study; mutants which grow slightly in the absence of growth factor are lost in the selection procedure or are often put aside. It is impossible to avoid wondering whether the selection of mutants has in some way resulted in a one-sided view of the phenomena.

It can be shown that certain mutants with an absolute growth requirement can make the substance they require in rather substantial quantities. Bonner, Yanofsky and Partridge (1952) were able to show that seven out of nine of the tryptophan-requiring mutants studied were able to make the substance required for growth, and in their work the possibility of synthesis by alternate pathways was definitely excluded. In our own laboratory it has been possible to show that a methionine-requiring strain, "blocked" between cystathionine and homocysteine, can make methionine from inorganic sulfate after only short periods of incubation in minimal medium (Strauss and Minagawa 1959). In other investigations it has been observed that certain mutants will not grow on minimal medium without long lag periods but that once growth begins it continues at an accelerating rate.

At least two different explanations other than the opening of alternate synthetic pathways can account for this ability to bypass the genetic block. Gene change in these cases may result in a quantitative deficiency in enzyme production or, as a result of the mutation, a qualitatively altered enzyme with lower efficiency may be produced. Obviously these alternatives are not mutually exclusive; there is no reason why gene mutation should not lead to either result in different cases. The end result of both explanations is the same—lowered enzyme activity. It can be shown experimentally that when the rate of production of a required growth substance is cut below a certain level, visible growth will not occur for long periods even though it is possible to detect the production of the required substance by the mutant (*l. c.*). Since the mutants studied represent a selected population to begin with, it is quite possible that a large proportion of the total mutant types produced are in fact "leaky." There is no way of deciding at present whether these represent cases of altered enzymes or whether many gene changes may result in quantitative rather than qualitative enzyme changes.

V. Complementation Phenomena

As was pointed out above, heterocaryons formed by two strains requiring different substances may supplement one another and grow on a minimal medium. For many years the evidence was consistent with the idea that if two biochemically deficient strains formed a heterocaryon which grew on minimal medium then the

22

genes affected were non-allelic and the biochemical reactions which they controlled were different. In fact, this heterocaryon test is a part of what may be called the functional test for the identity of two genes (Chapter 3). In the past several years, however, a number of cases have been described in which two mutants, *deficient in the same enzymatic step*, form heterocaryons which grow on minimal medium and produce the enzyme, albeit at a rate lower than the wild type. There is no evidence for any sort of gene recombination in these experiments and the interaction required to produce the enzyme must occur in the cytoplasm. As a result of the interaction two nuclei cooperate to "produce" an enzyme which neither could "produce" by itself. The meaning of "produce" is rather vague, of course, since the actual enzyme synthesis very likely occurs in the cytoplasm; very likely the term "determine" is somewhat better.

This phenomenon of complementation has been described for mutants which are unable to produce the enzyme adenylsuccinase (Giles, Partridge and Nelson 1957) and for those unable to produce glutamic dehydrogenase (Fincham 1958). Similar findings have been reported for mutants which require pantothenic acid in order to grow (Giles 1958). In all the cases studied the genes involved appear to be alleles (or very closely linked) by the standard test of genetic recombination. No recombinants have yet been recovered after crossing which can be unequivocably attributed to standard reciprocal recombination.

One of the interesting findings is that "complementation maps" may be constructed based on the ability of different alleles to form heterocaryons with one another. Such maps are constructed in a manner exactly analogous to the elucidation of the sequence of amino acids in a polypeptide chain by consideration of the types of dipeptides obtained. For example consider the case discussed by D. Woodward, Partridge and Giles (1958). If A, B and C are three mutations that complement each other and if D will complement with A but not with B or C and E will complement with C but not with A or B then the order must be ABC, and D must overlap B and C while E overlaps A and B. Logically consistent maps have been obtained from the three series of mutants studied but it is very difficult to decide exactly what these maps mean. Presumably they indicate some sort of linear, functional differentiation of the genetic material. More important, these findings seem to suggest some sort of recombination of gene products in the cytoplasm either to give active enzyme, or, more likely, to yield an active enzyme-producing system.

VI. Biochemical Mechanisms of Gene Interaction

So far we have mainly considered the effects of single gene changes on the single step reactions of metabolism. In most cases the experiments support the idea that there is a simple relationship between a single metabolic reaction and a single Mendelian gene. A few examples are not so easily disposed of. Some years ago Haskins and Mitchell (1952) and Newmeyer and Tatum (1933) studied the series of mutants which would respond to either indole, tryptophan or to nicotinic acid. Although the ability to grow on minimal medium segregated as though it were controlled by a single gene, the relative response to the different substances differed in the segregants from crosses to wild type as compared to the parents. The genetic interpretation of this type of phenomenon is that the response of the mutants is conditioned by the *genetic background*, that is, that there are genes present which will modify the response of the primary mutant gene. This is an example of gene interaction just as was the example of suppressor action mentioned earlier and it is desirable to discuss briefly the probable biochemical basis of gene interactions, or at any rate of the interactions of non-allelic genes.

First it is necessary to point out that there are certain definite principles which can be discerned from a study of metabolic reactions. The first of these has been assumed in most of our previous discussion; it seems self evident today but it is by no means trivial: The metabolism of compounds occurs in separate, discrete steps, each of which makes chemical sense. Each step reaction results in a relatively minor change to the molecule acted on but the net result of a series of steps is a large change. For example, in the metabolism of glucose the first step is a simple phosphorylation of one of the hydroxyl groups but as a result of a large number of steps the cyclic structure of the glucose molecule is degraded to carbon dioxide and water. Each step reaction is catalyzed by a specific enzyme and it is these enzymes which we assume are under genetic control. The separate step reactions are organized into chains or "multi-enzyme systems" (Dixon 1949). Organization is imposed on the system, even in homogeneous solution, by the *specificity* of the enzymes. Even in solution a highly ordered series of reactions such as those of alcoholic fermentation can occur because of this specificity. Not only are the individual reactions linked together by common substrates or products but the different multi-enzyme systems may be linked together by their use of common substrates, by mutual inhibition or by other mechanisms (Fig. 7). The whole of the metabolism of an organism can be considered as an interrelated system even though it is often convenient to consider the parts separately.

Organisms appear to have evolved control mechanisms which regulate the rates of reactions in many of the multi-enzyme systems. In mammals complex endocrine controls may determine the amounts of enzymes produced but even "simpler" organisms have developed satisfactory systems. A number of cases in which regulation occurs by negative feedback mechanisms have been described

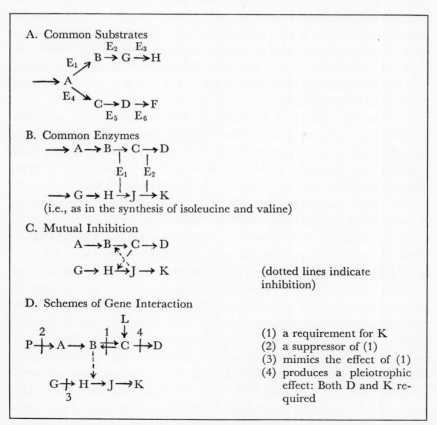

Figure 7. Possible methods of linking multi-enzyme systems. (After Strauss 1955.)

and it seems quite possible that this will turn out to be a general mechanism for biological reactions (Pardee 1959). In mechanisms of this sort the end product of a series of reactions acts to inhibit one of the earlier steps in the chain, thereby controlling the rate of its own formation. The inhibition may be either inhibition of enzyme formation or of enzyme action. For example Yates and Pardee (1957) have shown that uracil will inhibit the formation of pyrimidine intermediates earlier than orotic acid. Gorini and Maas (1957) showed that arginine inhibits the synthesis of the enzyme, ornithine transcarbamylase, which is necessary for the synthesis of arginine in E. coli. Findings of this type help explain why microorganisms will preferentially utilize amino acids supplied in the medium instead of synthesizing their own. From the viewpoint of general biology it is not at all surprising that microorganisms should regulate their reaction rates by mechanisms depending on inhibition since the use of such mechanisms is a common occurrence in all phases of biology. The control of the heart beat, one of the simpler regulatory mechanisms, is the result, in part, of inhibition of the heart by discharge of the vagus nerve. In endocrinology in particular there are many cases of regulations by mutual inhibitions.

Because the whole of metabolism can be thought of as interrelated it is useful to think of the total of the reaction pathways in an organism as in a state of "balance" (Strauss 1955, 1956). Any upset in the balanced condition may lead to unexpected effects. The succinate-requiring mutants of Neurospora require a dicarboxylic acid because of a deficiency in carbon dioxide fixation. Spores of the mutant suspended in buffer can metabolize sugars in a normal manner without the accumulation of any intermediates. Addition of a nitrogen source such as ammonia that can be utilized for synthetic purposes changes the situation. Addition of ammonium ion results in an inhibition of oxygen uptake and in the accumulation of various partially oxidized products of carbohydrate metabolism such as acetoin and alphaketoisovaleric acid.

The dicarboxylic acids are used for two major purposes in metabolism; first, they catalyze the oxidation of carboydrate by the Krebs tricarboxylic acid cycle and, second, they serve as intermediates for the synthesis of a variety of compounds such as the amino acids and the porphyrins. Ordinarily the supply of dicarboxylic acid used for synthetic purposes is replenished by carbon dioxide fixation but this is not possible in the succinate-requiring mutants. In the absence of ammonium ion no lesion is observed because of the precarious balance between supply and demand for catalytic purposes. Removal of substrate quantities of material initiated by the addition of ammonium ion leads to an inhibition of the tricarboxylic acid cycle with a subsequent accumulation of partially oxidized products of carbohydrate metabolism. The feature of this accumulation is that it is *not* the result of the accumulation of intermediates behind a genetic block but is rather a result of the interrelations of metabolic pathways.

Now if genes control the step reactions of metabolism which are themselves organized into multi-enzyme systems and if these systems interact, then the genes which control the step reactions will also appear to interact. The gene interaction obtained in these cases is not really an interaction of the genes themselves but is rather an interaction of the gene-controlled step reactions in nongenic parts of the organism. This idea can be documented by studies on certain suppressor genes. Suppressors have been discussed before in connection with the tryptophan-requiring mutants. The suppressed *td* mutants have enzyme activity not present in the non-suppressed mutant but the suppressor gene does not duplicate the wild type allele and it is necessary to conclude that the specificity of the system still resides with the *td* allele.

One of the best known of the suppressor systems is a single gene suppressor in Drosophila which will suppress the mutants vermilion, sable and spot. Since vermilion in Drosophila has a phenotype resulting from a block in tryptophan metabolism and since sable and spot have changes in melanin formation (melanin is formed as a result of tyrosine oxidation by tyrosinase) the occurrence of a single genetic system that suppresses the three mutations simultaneously is probably evidence for some unknown relationship between the pathways of tryptophan and tyrosine metabolism. The suppressor restores the ability of flies to make kynurenine from tryptophan but the mechanisms involved must be of fairly complex nature since it is known that starvation of the larvae will permit this reaction to occur to some extent.

It is my opinion that in most cases suppressors act by introducing a second genetic block into the metabolic system and that in some way this second lesion compensates for the effect of the first. This type of mechanism has been demonstrated with mutants of Neurospora that require acetate for growth (Strauss and Pierog 1954). These mutants are inhibited by hexose sugars such as glucose but will grow with pentoses if acetate is added to the medium. Two different, non-allelic modifiers or suppressors (the definition depends more on the degree of effect than on any real difference) relieve the inhibition and permit some growth in the absence of added acetate. Both of these suppressor genes act to lower the activity of pyruvic carboxylase. As far as is known this is a quantitative effect; the pyruvic carboxylase from mutant strains seems qualitatively identical with the wild type enzyme. Lowering the pyruvic carboxylase activity reduces the amount of acetaldehyde formed from glucose in the mutant strains and it seems likely that acetaldehyde or some derivative is the cause of the glucose inhibition. The small quantities of acetaldehyde that are still formed are oxidized to acetate directly, providing a shunt around the blocked reaction and permitting some growth in the absence of added acetate. The suppressor genes restore the organism towards the wild type by introducing a second block which lowers the production of an inhibitor accumulating because of the primary lesion. As indicated above the fact that many non-allelic suppressor genes can restore the ability of certain of the *td* alleles to produce an active tryptophan synthetase (Suskind and Kurek 1959) has been explained in this way.

This may be too facile a description of the problem and it should not be considered that the basic mode of action of all suppressors or modifiers is definitively known. Cystathionine is split by two different enzymes in Neurospora. Cystathionase I splits the compound into cysteine and homoserine, cystathionase II splits the compound on the other side of the sulfur atom to give homocysteine and serine (Fig. 1). Both these enzymes may be affected by different mutations. One strain, blocked between cystathionine and homocysteine, lacks cystathionase II; another strain, unable to form cystathionine from cysteine, lacks cystathionase I. Apparently therefore the reaction catalyzed by the enzyme is reversible and the cystathionase I system is involved in the biosynthesis of cystathionine (Fischer 1957).

A single gene suppressor is known which restores the ability of the strain blocked between cystathionine and homocysteine to grow in the absence of added methionine (the product in this chain of metabolic reactions) (Giles 1951). As expected this suppressor restores the ability of the mutant strain to make cystathionase II. What is not expected is that the same suppressor will also suppress the strain unable to form cystathionine from cysteine and will restore the ability of this strain to produce cysta-thionase I. There is no interpretation of this finding based on experimental evidence. The two enzymes obviously have similar specificities since both use cystathionine as a substrate, but whether this is related to the mechanism of action of the suppressor gene is just not known.

VII. *Organized Enzyme Systems*

There can be little doubt that the step reactions of metabolism are subject to genetic control by means of the genetic control over the activity and structure of particular enzymes. Since the individual step reactions form systems which interact by direct and indirect mechanisms, gene mutation may also have effects on metabolism which are far removed from the original or direct site of gene action.

We have been considering only the system of soluble enzymes upon which the structure of modern biochemistry is based. These substances are individual protein molecules which exist free in solution. Green and Järnefelt (1959) have pointed out that the enzyme systems which are organized in the matrix of the mitochondria may not really have an individual existence in the same sense as those soluble proteins most often studied. There may be new principles of enzymology to be discovered in the study of these organized systems and if so, then there are new principles of chemical genetics yet to be elucidated. The organized structure that is of most interest to geneticists is, of course, the chromosome and there are experiments which indicate that the chromosomes may be organized for sequential chemical reactions in the same sense as the mitochondria. One type of phenomenon can be studied only with diploids, that is with organisms containing two doses of a particular chromosome. These may be true diploids as in the case of flies and man or they may be heterocaryons or even bacteria infected with more than one virus particle. In some cases it is found that the phenotype of an organism containing two mutant factors depends on whether the factors occur together on one chromosome with two normal alternatives on the other chromosome or whether one mutant factor occurs on each chromosome. The two situations may be represented as follows: either ab//++ (called the *cis* configuration in analogy with geometrical isomerism in organic chemistry) or a+//+b (the *trans* configuration). In Drosophila, in

29

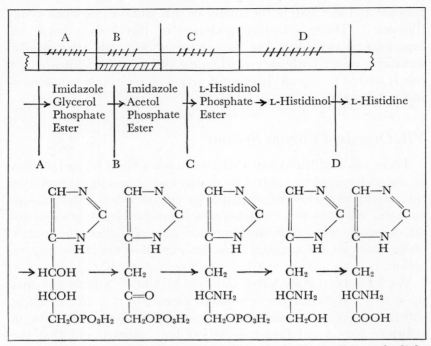

Figure 8. The order of four histidine loci (*hi*-A, -B, -C, -D) on the linkage map of Salmonella. Probable relation of genetic blocks with the proposed primary pathway of L-histidine synthesis is indicated by the arrows. (Hartman, Carnegie Inst. Wash. Publ. No. 612, 1956).

Aspergillus and in other organisms there are a number of cases in which the *trans* configuration has a mutant phenotype although the *cis* configuration is normal. The genetic meaning of this phenomenon will be discussed in a later chapter, but this is obviously a case in which the function of a gene depends on its position. According to the idea suggested by Lewis (1951) some sort of intermediate is acted on in a sequential manner by the chromosome. The intermediate is restricted in its properties so that it is unable to diffuse from one chromosome to the second. This condition results in a failure to form any end product when there is a single lesion in each chromosome. Location of both lesions in a single chromosome will permit formation of the end product on the second, normal chromosome.

The explanation was developed to explain findings obtained with certain morphological and eye color mutants of Drosophila. The biochemistry of the mutations is essentially unknown and at this stage the explanation, while plausible, does not suggest further experiments. Recently however evidence has been obtained using the bacterium Salmonella which supports the Lewis idea of the functional differentiation of the chromosomes (Demerec and Hartman 1956, Hartman 1956). Geneticists have long wondered whether the factors that occur linked together have some functional relationship or whether the location of the genes in relation to one another is a matter of pure chance. The early work with Neurospora gave no support to the idea that the linkage relationships of the genes had any relationship to the biochemical reactions controlled by the genes. In Salmonella however the genes controlling the biosynthesis of histidine are arranged in the same sequence as are the reactions involved in histidine biosynthesis (Fig. 8); several cases of this type have been described. It is difficult to avoid the hope that this arrangement is not itself a matter of pure chance and to search for some reason why the linkage group or chromosomes of Salmonella should be organized differently from those of the higher organisms. Once again the answer is not known but it is apparent that in some organisms the relationship between genes and enzymes may be spatial as well as informational.

Genetics as a science correlates phenotypic effects with breeding experiments. We know that "genes" control enzymes because, in a cross, certain definite ratios of progeny with enzyme and with no enzyme are obtained. On the other hand there is very little evidence indicating how this genetic control of enzyme structure is exerted. We suppose that the substance deoxyribonucleic acid is the carrier of the genetic information and we suppose further that the information is transferred from the nucleus to the site of protein synthesis. However there is still no experiment which demonstrates a specific role for deoxyribonucleic acid in the process of protein synthesis and so we are still in ignorance about the physiological basis of the genetic control of protein synthesis.

Chapter Two

The Chemical Nature of the
Hereditary Material

In *all likelihood* the chemical basis of inheritance can be ascribed to a single substance, deoxyribonucleic acid or DNA. The idea that this substance carries within its structure the genetic information passed from parent to offspring pervades all of modern thinking about genetics. I would like to examine some of the evidence for the concept and to discuss the structure of the material, DNA, and the mechanism by which it is duplicated and transferred to daughter cells. In the next chapter I will attempt to demonstrate how modern studies on the "fine structure" of the gene, using purely genetic techniques (breeding experiments), can be interpreted in terms of the structure of DNA first suggested by Watson and Crick.

I. Indirect Evidence

The evidence for the role of DNA in inheritance is of two types: one line of evidence based on correlation between the properties of the genetic material and of DNA and the other based on more direct experiments. If DNA is genetic material it should be

TABLE 3.   *Constancy of DNA per Nucleus and Correlation of the Amount of DNA with the Number of Chromosome Sets*

*DNA Content ($\mu\mu$g. per nucleus) of Nuclei of Diploid Cells and Sperm in Several Species**

SPECIES	ERYTHROCYTE	LIVER	SPERM
Domestic fowl	2.34	2.39	1.26
Shad	1.97	2.01	0.91
Carp	3.49	3.33	1.64
Brown trout	5.79		2.67
Toad	7.33		3.70

* From Vendrely, in Chargaff and Davidson, Editors, The Nucleic Acids, Academic Press, Inc., 1955, vol. 2.

located exclusively at the location of the genes and its quantity should be proportional to the number of the genes (Mazia 1952). DNA is located exclusively in cell nuclei. (There have been reports of a DNA reserve in the cytoplasm of certain eggs (frogs, sea urchins) sufficient to allow for a few cleavages, but the existence of this reserve is not established with certainty (Brachet 1957).) The amount of DNA per cell nucleus is relatively constant. Although the content of ribonucleic acid (RNA) and of protein may change drastically with changes in the physiological condition of the cell, the DNA content remains constant as is expected if the DNA content reflects the gene number. (However it is possible to cause statistically significant changes in the DNA content by certain hormonal treatments, *l.c.*) There is a correlation between the number of chromosome sets and amount of DNA (Table 3). For example, haploid cells have about one half the amount of DNA found in diploid cells and the DNA per cell increases in multiples of the haploid amount rather than by fractional amounts as the cells become polyploid. But these relationships are not exact. There are several reports indicating that there may be small changes in DNA content as a result of various treatments and that therefore the content may not be exactly proportional to the gene number (assuming that the gene number does not change during the physiological activity of the cell). Nevertheless, the content and location of DNA are more closely correlated with the genes than are these attributes of any other cellular constituent (Vendrely 1955).

Many experiments indicate that DNA, once formed, is metabolically inert and does not "turn over" or participate in cellular metabolism to the same extent as do other cellular constituents, particularly RNA. Several authors suppose that this metabolic inertness is further evidence for the genetic role of DNA since, they reason, the genetic material which must serve as a storehouse of information should remain "aloof" from the day to day business of the cell (Mazia 1952). The fact of the inertness of DNA is certainly definite and radioactive material incorporated into DNA can therefore be used as a permanent label for the DNA, but the force of this particular argument has never seemed very great to me.

An additional type of experiment has been much quoted as indicating a genetic role for DNA. Ultraviolet radiation is definitely mutagenic and it appears that there is a definite correlation between the absorption spectrum of nucleic acid and the action spectrum for mutation. This observation has been interpreted as indicating that the nucleic acid is the target molecule and that the changes resulting in the nucleic acid have resulted in mutation. But the exact point of the maximum efficiency of ultraviolet radiation varies with different organisms (Wagner and Mitchell 1955). In addition, there are a variety of investigations showing that energy absorbed by one molecule can migrate both within and between molecules before producing any effects (Aronoff 1957). The action spectrum experiments are perhaps necessary but certainly not sufficient to implicate DNA as the genetic substance.

It is obvious that the observations outlined above do no more than suggest that DNA would be a likely candidate for the genetic material. In the period before about 1940 most geneticists (if they accepted the idea that genetic material could be described in molecular terms) would have supposed that the genetic material was protein in nature. At that time it was supposed that DNA was a polytetranucleotide, a polymer of a repeating unit of four nucleotides, and that the DNA structure did not provide enough variation to account for genetic specificity which, it was supposed, must therefore depend on protein. The proteins had been demonstrated to provide specificity to enzymes, antibodies and to hormones and it was simple to extrapolate their action to include the genes.

Recently it has been realized that although DNA does contain regularities in structure, there are differences in the base ratios, particularly between different species, and it is now supposed that the nucleotides occur in random order and are not arranged as

35

repeating tetranucleotides (Chargaff 1955). Variation in the order of the bases therefore provides an adequate alphabet for the storage of genetic information.

II. *Transformation in Bacteria*

The real experimental evidence that forces exclusive consideration of DNA as the genetic material comes from studies with microorganisms, particularly from studies on the transforming principle of bacteria. The pneumococci ordinarily possess a smooth polysaccharide coat which accounts for their serological specificity and which gives colonies of this organism a smooth (s) glistening appearance on agar plates. Occasionally after culture *in vitro*, cells are obtained which yield colonies in which the polysaccharide is not produced and which have a rough (R) appearance. This s → R transformation is irreversible; R cells never spontaneously develop the ability to make polysaccharide. In 1928 Griffith discovered that the injection into animals of heat killed s cells along with the viable R cells, leading to the production, *in vivo*, of viable s-type cells containing a polysaccharide coat of a serological type characteristic of the s type injected. This phenomenon is called transformation and was later obtained *in vitro*. In 1944 Avery, McCleod and MacCarty isolated the substance responsible for the type specific transformation and showed that it was deoxyribonucleic acid. Later the transformation phenomenon was obtained with *Hemophilus influenzae* (Alexander and Leidy 1951) and recently transformation has been obtained with *Bacillus subtilis* (Spizizen 1958) and in Xanthomonas (Corey and Starr 1957). Transformation is not restricted to the capsular polysaccharides; transformation of drug resistance, biochemical (or nutritional) characteristics and of ability to make an adaptive enzyme has been achieved (Hotchkiss 1955).

The evidence is quite good that the transforming principle is really DNA uncontaminated by protein (Zamenhof 1957). The best transforming preparations obtained contain less than 0.02 per cent of protein. It has been estimated that the amount of DNA required to transform one cell of *Hemophilus influenzae* is about 10^{-8} μg. If we assume a protein content in these preparations of as much as 0.01 per cent then this amount of DNA corresponds to 6 protein molecules of 100,000 molecular weight or less than one protein molecule of molecular weight 1,000,000. On purely analytical grounds it is therefore possible to eliminate the possibility that protein plays a specific role in the transformation process. There is an impressive correlation between the action of agents which degrade or react with DNA, *i.e.* the enzyme deoxyribonuclease (often written DNAase) which catalyzes the hydrolysis of DNA, and the effect of such agents in destroying transforming activity. Proteolytic enzymes and those degrading ribonucleic acid have no effect on transforming activity.

The system for transformation in pneumococcus is quite complex and in most cases only a small proportion of the total number of cells present are transformed. As originally described by Avery and his co-workers (1944) the transformation system contained nutrient broth and serum or serous fluid in addition to the bacteria and transforming principle. These components can be eliminated with Hemophilus; it is possible to obtain transformation of Hemophilus in buffer (but the cells are grown on a complex medium). With pneumococcus the cells must be in a particularly receptive or "competent" state, determined partly by their stage in the growth cycle (Hotchkiss 1954). Since P-32 labeled DNA is fixed by the recipient cells the added DNA is actually incorporated into the recipient organism (cf. Lerman and Tolmach 1957).

The salient point that transformation is a true genetic change can be seen from the following experiment: Mannitol dehydrogenase is a diphosphopyridine-linked adaptive enzyme which confers upon cells the ability to use mannitol as a carbon source. Non-adapted cells do not possess enzyme activity but will develop activity upon addition of mannitol to the medium *if* the cells are of the proper genetic type. Certain pneumococcus strains have been obtained which lack the ability to respond to the addition of mannitol by the production of enzyme. Transforming principle (DNA) prepared from either adapted or non-adapted cells of a type genetically capable of producing the enzyme will transfer the ability to make the enzyme when the recipient cells are placed in a suitable environment containing mannitol. Once transformed the cells retain the ability to respond to mannitol and transmit this ability to their descendents. The DNA has therefore transferred the ability to produce an enzyme forming system as an inherited characteristic (Hotchkiss 1956).

Although many characteristics may be transformed, in general these are transformed only one at a time. If recipient (R) cells are treated with DNA obtained from an encapsulated (s), streptomycin resistant organism only one or the other property is trans-

TABLE 4. *Evidence of Linkage between Mannitol and Strepto-mycin Resistance Characters in Pneumococcus Trans-forming Principle**

CHARACTERS PRESENT IN		CHARACTERS FOUND IN TRANSFORMANTS		
DONOR DNA	RECIPIENT CELL	SINGLE		DOUBLE
M S†	m s‡	M s	m S	many M S
M s + m S	m s	M s**	m S**	fewer than random M S
M s	m S	M S	(m s)§	many M s
m S	M s	M S	(m s)	many m S
M s P	m s p	M s p**	m s P	fewer than random M s P

* From Hotchkiss, in Gaebler, Editor, Enzymes, Academic Press, Inc., 1956.
† Characters: M = mannitol utilizing
                S = streptomycin resistant
                P = penicillin resistant
‡ Small letters signify absence of the corresponding property.
§ Phenotypes in parentheses were difficult to detect and were not observed.
** These genotypes could also result from double transformation.

formed at a time, very rarely both. In the above example R resistant or s sensitive cells would be obtained but only rarely would s resistant cells be obtained. The frequency with which the rare double transformations occur is about equal to the product of the frequencies of the single transformation, indicating that two independent events are involved. This type of experiment indicates that only a portion of the total potential material contained in the donor DNA is actually incorporated into the host in any one event. Transformation therefore does not involve a complete substitution of one set of genes for another.

There is evidence for genetic complexity, or linkage, in transforming principle preparations (Table 4). If recipient organisms are treated with DNA obtained from streptomycin-resistant, mannitol-utilizing pneumococcus cells it is observed that double transformants occur much more frequently than would be expected if two independent events were involved (*l. c.*). This is evidence that genetic factors can occur linked in isolated DNA preparations. Since, as will be seen, the phenomenon of linkage is basic to genetics this observation shows that DNA has the very special property required of a genetic substance.

Transformation first appeared to represent a case of directed mutation brought about by a specific substance. This opinion is

38

no longer fashionable and it is believed that transformation represents a method of genetic recombination analogous to the gene recombination that occurs as a feature of sexual reproduction. Transforming principles may carry the determinants for two or more characters. These may be transmitted singly and independently or, as indicated above, two characters may be transmitted together by transformation more often than would be expected by chance. This is the same sort of linkage that is found in higher organisms during the known processes of gene transmission. It seems simpler to assume that transformation represents a queer but definite method of gene transfer, and that the DNA (genetic material) of the donor, when introduced into the recipient cell, becomes a part of recipient genetic material by some method related to the normal mechanisms for the incorporation of genetic material. This viewpoint has the advantage that it makes some of the features of virus infection appear as aspects of the same phenomenon.

III. *Studies with Viruses*

It was the hope of many geneticists that the smaller organisms would provide the best material for study of the nature of the gene. It was expected that these organisms must in some way be simpler than the multicellular plants and animals. A great deal of information has been obtained from the bacteria and from the even smaller viruses, but it would be difficult today to convince anyone that these organisms are fundamentally simpler than any others. In some ways they may be even more specialized; they have presumably had as long an evolutionary history as the larger organisms and their small size does conceal a remarkable amount of genetic complexity.

The virulent bacteriophages are viruses which reproduce within a bacterial cell (Adams 1959). The viruses that have been studied most are the coliphages of the T series; these viruses attack the common colon bacillus *Escherichia coli*. Although small, the viruses of the "T even" series, T2, T4 and T6 have a definite morphology and have a tadpole shaped appearance when viewed with the electron microscope. They also have a definite chemical structure with a protein outer coat surrounding a core of DNA. The DNA from certain of the virus strains has a very distinctive composition and can be recognized by the substitution of hydroxy-

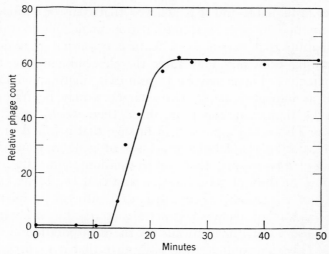

Figure 9. A one-step growth experiment with bacteriophage T1 on *Escherichia coli*, strain B, in nutrient broth at 37° C. Phage and bacteria, at a ratio 1:10, were mixed at time 0. The mixture was diluted after 4 minutes, when 45 per cent of the phage had been absorbed. Assays were made at intervals after dilution. Average phage yield per infected cell = 62 × 100/45 = 138. (Luria, General Virology, John Wiley & Sons, Inc., 1953).

methylcystosine for cytosine and by the presence of nucleotides containing glucose (*l. c.*, Sinsheimer 1954).

The virulent phages lyse their host at the conclusion of the infective period and this lysis is the basis for quantitative estimation of the number of phage particles. A suspension of phage and bacteria (containing a large excess of bacteria) is plated on an agar plate. The bacteria grow and eventually cover the plate with a translucent carpet of bacterial growth. The point at which a virus particle or an infected bacterium has been plated appears as a hole in the carpet since each infected bacterium will lyse with the elimination of virus progeny. These infect the surrounding bacteria which lyse in turn and the process is continued until a visible hole or *plaque* can be seen in the cover of bacterial growth. Since the efficiency with which a single virus particle leads to the formation of a plaque is very high, counting the number of plaques gives a very good estimate of the number of virus particles. Different virus strains give plaques with different characteristics and mutant types may be recognized by changes in the type of plaque produced (Luria 1953).

The start of modern studies on bacterial viruses was the "single-

40

step growth experiment" (Fig. 9) (Ellis and Delbruck 1939, Delbruck and Luria 1942). A bacterial suspension is infected with virus at time zero so that there is a large excess of bacteria and then diluted with an antiphage antibody to stop further phage adsorption and remove unadsorbed virus. Portions of the medium are removed at various time periods and the total number of virus particles is determined. It is found that for a period of from about thirteen to twenty-one minutes (or longer, depending on the virus strain) there is no change in the number of particles, then within a short period there is a large increase in the number of virus particles —as much as a 300 fold increase may be observed—after which the number of virus particles again remains constant for a period equivalent to the original latent period. The problem is to determine what happens within the bacteria during the latent period.

One surprising fact was discovered fairly early in the study of virus biochemistry and genetics. If a bacterium is infected with a virus and then if the bacterium-virus combination is experimentally disrupted shortly after the infection has begun, the original virus particle *cannot* be recovered (Doermann, 1952). About ten minutes after infection (depending on the strain and on conditions) complete virus particles begin to appear and they increase in number until the bacterium lyses. The existence of this *eclipse* period indicates that whatever does get into the bacterium is not complete virus during the early stages of infection. Finally, although the virus is small it is genetically complex. Many loci have been identified (the genetic properties of ability to infect particular strains (host range) or plaque morphology can be used as genetic markers) and these are linked together as are the genes of larger organisms, probably in one linkage group although the earlier studies supposed three linkage groups for phage T2. Mating experiments with bacteriophage are performed by infecting a single bacterium with two virus particles of different genetic type. If the virus particles are closely enough related "mating" occurs and recombinant virus progeny are obtained (Adams 1959).

Suspension of virus particles in concentrated salt solution followed by rapid dilution results in the breakup of the virus due to osmotic shock (Table 5). This treatment solubilizes the DNA while the major portion of the phage protein remains as a "ghost" that can be sedimented in the ultracentrifuge and can still react with phage antiserum (Herriott 1951). A second point of importance is that the tadpole shaped viruses attach to the bacterium

TABLE 5. *The Chemical Differentiation of Bacteriophage. Composition of Ghosts and Solution of Plasmolyzed Phage**

	PER CENT OF ISOTOPE			
	WHOLE PHAGE LABELED WITH		PLASMOLYZED PHAGE LABELED WITH	
	P^{32}	S^{35}	P^{32}	S^{35}
Acid soluble	—	—	1	—
Acid soluble after treatment with DNAase	1	1	80	1
Adsorbed to sensitive bacteria	85	90	2	90
Precipitated by antiphage serum	90	99	5	97

* From Hershey and Chase, J. Gen. Physiol., vol. 36, 1952.

by their tails. The phage-bacterium connection can be broken by the shearing action supplied by a Waring Blendor.

The phage particle contains both DNA and the protein. Is the genetic message carried by only one substance or do both share this function? Hershey and Chase (1952) approached the question as follows: If phages are produced by infecting bacteria growing in medium containing labeled sulfate ($S^{35}O_4$) the sulfur of the virus will be labeled which means that only the protein will contain isotope since the DNA contains no sulfur. Growth with P-32 labeled phosphate will label mainly the DNA and not the protein. In the experiment bacteria are infected with labeled phages and the phage-bacterium connection is broken after a short time by the shearing action of the Waring Blendor. If infection has proceeded for several minutes before the application of the Waring Blendor, progeny virus particles will be produced. When P-32 labeled phage particles are used, the P-32 enters the bacterium and a fraction of the label can be recovered in the progeny phage. On the average about 30 to 50 per cent of the parental P-32 is transferred to the progeny. When S-35 labeled phage is used less than 5 per cent of the label is transferred to the bacterium and none of the label appears in the progeny. This experiment is generally interpreted to mean that the genetic information of the phage is contained in the DNA, since practically no protein is injected and only the phosphorus (= DNA) is transferred to progeny. Since the 5 per cent of sulfur transfer represented, in part anyhow, the limits of the experimental technique it was sometimes supposed (but not by Hershey) that the experiment indicated that no protein was transferred to the host bacterium. Hershey (1955) has subsequently shown that there is a protein component amounting to about 3 per cent of the total phage protein which does not sediment with the "ghosts" and which is (probably) injected into the infected bacterium. This protein is *not* passed on to the progeny phage and its function is not known.

It has been demonstrated that some protein synthesis (other than that required for the synthesis of hydroxymethyl cytosine— a special component of phages T2, T4 and T6) must occur before phage DNA can be formed (Watanabe *et al.* 1958). In addition there is a synthesis of a fraction of the ribonucleic acid (RNA) of the bacterium-virus complex immediately after infection. The RNA synthesized after phage infection has a composition different from that of the host bacterium; its composition is similar to that of the *virus* DNA with uracil substituted for thymine (see below, Chapter 5). Free bacteriophage particles do not contain RNA.

There is evidence, discussed later in this chapter, that indicates that at a stage in virus infection genetic information is passed to a molecule in which phosphorus does not occupy a key position (Stent 1955). It is possible that protein may have some role in the transfer of information but there is no doubt that the Hershey and Chase experiment is strong evidence that DNA is a genetic substance, probably *the* genetic substance.

Not all of the viruses contain DNA although all do contain nucleic acid of some type. Tobacco mosaic virus (TMV) and the related plant viruses contain a ribonucleic acid (RNA) component (Schramm 1958). RNA differs from DNA in the substitution of the pentose ribose for deoxyribose and in the use of the pyrimidine uracil instead of thymine. There are also differences in the three dimensional structure. Tobacco mosaic virus was crystallized by Stanley in 1936 and is usually quoted as an example of a "simple" virus. The very fact of the crystallization of an infectious principle set off a debate as to the definition of the terms "life" and "living" which it is quite impossible to settle satisfactorily (Pirie 1937). Are stable crystals to be considered alive, or do non-living substances reproduce their own kind when placed in a suitable environment?

The relative chemical simplicity of these viruses does permit investigations of their structure. The tobacco mosaic virus has a central core of RNA surrounded by a protein coat; no other constituents have been detected. It is possible to separate the protein and the nucleic acid from each other by treatment with dodecyl sulfate or similar agents and either the protein or nucleic acid can be prepared in "native" form (Fraenkel-Conrat and Williams 1955). The protein from related strains of virus may have different amino acid compositions. Protein prepared from the Holmes Ribgrass HR strain contains histidine and methionine but these substances are absent from the usual TMV strain.

It is quite definitely established that separated virus RNA has a certain residual infectivity which is not the result of whole virus impurity in the preparations (Gierer and Schramm 1956, Fraenkel-Conrat *et al.* 1957). This infectivity is susceptible to the action of ribonuclease in contrast to the resistance of the native virus and the activity is also unstable on standing in solution at room temperatures at which the native virus is stable. The addition of separately prepared virus protein to the virus RNA preparation leads to a large restoration of activity and to a preparation which is no longer susceptible to ribonuclease action. Such preparations have the shape of TMV in the electron microscope and it is quite possible that the virus has been reconstituted from its parts. However the data can also be interpreted as indicating that the infectious RNA is protected against inactivation by the addition of a protein coat (Schramm 1958).

The fact that "naked" RNA is infectious indicates that all of the genetic information must be carried by the RNA (since as a result of infection complete virus is produced) and that the protein portion must serve to protect the RNA and increase its infectivity. This conclusion is confirmed by the following elegant experiment (which was done before it was realized that the residual infectivity of RNA was a real property of the RNA and was not due to contamination): Artificial hybrids were made by reconstituting HR protein with TMV nucleic acid and by mixing TMV protein with HR nucleic acid. The "artificial" virus which resulted was applied to susceptible plants and the constitution of the protein of the progeny virus was determined. The protein coat formed was always characteristic of the nucleic acid of the infecting virus, never of the original protein, indicating that the genetic information was carried exclusively by the nucleic acid (Fraenkel-Conrat and Singer 1957). In the case of the plant viruses the nucleic acid is RNA.

Certain bacterial viruses can transfer genetic properties from their host as a donor to a recipient. These virus particles are not of the highly virulent type, and the process, called *transduction,* has been observed in Salmonella and in *E. coli* (Hartman 1957). In transduction a fragment of the nuclear genetic material of the host is carried by the virus from one cell to another. The phenomenon is very useful in microbial genetics because it can be used to determine the relative location of the genetic factors (mapping) in organisms in which mating does not occur. If the only significant material injected into the infected bacterium by the virus is DNA (as is the case with the virulent virus studied by Hershey and Chase) this transduction phenomenon is evidence that the *bacterial* genetic material is DNA. Obviously this evidence is not nearly as convincing as that obtained with the transforming principle but it should be clear that transduction and transformation are aspects of the same problem.

IV. *Transmutation Techniques*

The beta decay of radioactive isotopes such as P-32 is accompanied by two physical effects. First there is the emission of a beta particle and, in any experiment in which high specific activities of isotope are used, the possibility of radiation damage by the beta particles must be considered. In addition the elimination of a beta particle from the atomic nucleus results in a change in the atomic number of the element which results in a change in its chemical nature. This transformation of elements has been called *transmutation* since the time of the alchemists. In the case of phosphorus the recoil energy derived from the ejection of the beta particle may cause the atomic nucleus itself to recoil. If a radioactive P-32 atom decays while the atom is a part of the DNA molecule it is possible that the molecule will be damaged. The product of transmutation would be S-32; sulfur esters of the type formed are not stable in water solution and the probability of recoil is very high (Strauss 1958). Some time ago it was shown that bacteriophage labeled with P-32 of high specific activity tended to die off much faster than would be expected on the basis of the radiation accompanying the decay. It was estimated that about ten disintegrations of P-32 were required to inactivate a single phage particle (Hershey *et al.* 1951).

Mutants of *Escherichia coli* requiring thymine for growth have the ability to synthesize RNA and protein when they are incubated in a minimal medium but DNA is synthesized only when the growth factor is added (Cohen and Barner 1954). Using this

45

thymine-requiring bacterium Fuerst and Stent (1957) were able to show that the decay of P-32 incorporated into DNA ($+$ RNA $+$ protein) was much more lethal than when the same amount of P-32 was incorporated into RNA $+$ protein alone. Later it was shown that the loss of the ability to make a variety of enzymes was perfectly correlated with the decay of phosphorus in the DNA, which shows that integrity of the DNA is required for normal protein formation (McFall, Pardee and Stent 1958).

One of the major achievements of modern genetics, ranking with the clarification of the relationship between genes and metabolic processes by Beadle and Tatum, was the discovery of recombination or mating in bacteria by Lederberg (1947). He showed that the mixing of particular strains of E. coli with complementary growth requirements could result in the formation of wild type, or prototrophic strains. A mixture of $A^+B^-C^+D^+$ and $A^-B^+C^-D^-$ would occasionally yield bacteria with no growth requirements, that is $A^+B^+C^+D^+$. A great deal of further study has shown that this process of recombination in bacteria involves an exchange of cell material following conjugation. The exchange is unidirectional in nature. There are two mating types termed F^+ and F^- and the genetic material is always transferred from $+$ to $-$, never the reverse. The process is actually more complex than indicated here. Genetic exchange occurs at low frequency except in certain *Hfr* strains in which the frequency with which *particular* genes are exchanged is high. Transfer is always from *Hfr* to $-$.

Genetic recombination in the *Hfr* strains can be affected by P-32 decay (Jacob and Wollman 1958). In one type of experiment *Hfr* strains are grown in medium containing P-32 of high specific activity and are then mated with non-labeled F^- strains. The zygotes are stored in the frozen condition to permit P-32 decay to take place. It is found that the number of recombinants obtained diminishes with P-32 decay, indicating the destruction of genetic material which can be integrated into the genome of the recipient. In a second type of experiment the labeled *Hfr* strains are stored prior to mating. In bacteria the linkage group from the donor enters the recipient in a geometrically ordered way, one portion always entering first. Storage of the labeled strains prior to mating decreases the size of the piece that can enter the recipient and participate in recombination. These experiments are further evidence that the genetic material contains phosphorus in a key

46

position. It has not been possible to obtain decay effects (on viability) in Neurospora with radioactive sulfur-35 which upon beta decay is transmuted to chlorine-35 (Strauss 1959). It is therefore reasonable to suppose that the genetic material contains phosphorus in a key position but not sulfur; that is, is more likely to contain nucleic acid than protein.

V. The Structure of DNA

If the DNA molecule carries genetic information then there must be something unique about its structure which fits the substance for its role. The genetic properties which must be accounted for in any molecular structure are those of linearity (the linear arrangements of the genes in the linkage groups), of reproduction (the ability of the genetic material to make the cell fashion copies of itself), the ability to change or to mutate, and the ability to make the cell do something as a result of the presence of the particular molecular configuration.

Hydrolysis of preparations of DNA yields the deoxynucleotides of adenine, guanine, cytosine and thymine. (See the compendium edited by Chargaff and Davidson (1955) for details.) In the T2, T4 and T6 bacteriophage of E. coli 5-hydroxymethylcytosine takes the place of cytosine while in wheat germ about one-quarter of the cytosine is replaced by methylcytosine. Glucose has been reported as a constituent of the DNA of certain bacteriophages (Sinsheimer 1954). There are differences in the base ratios of DNA preparations from different species; that is the molar amounts of adenine, guanine, cytosine and thymine are not 1:1:1:1 as required by the old tetranucleotide hypothesis of DNA structure, but there are definite analytical regularities. The ratio of adenine to thymine and of guanine to cytosine seems always to equal one. (There are reports by Bendich and his collaborators (1956) that in the chromatographic separation of DNA, certain fractions were found to have ratios of guanine to cytosine which differed from the expected 1.0 and these regularities were not found in DNA prepared from phage ϕX174 (Sinsheimer 1959).) The RNA preparations examined do not display as much regularity but there does seem to be an equivalence of 6-keto and 6-amino groups.

In 1953 Watson and Crick (1953 a, b, c) suggested a structure for DNA which has had almost revolutionary consequences for thinking about the problems of biology. Their structure was based

47

on the construction of molecular models arranged to conform to the physical characteristics of the DNA molecule. Chemical evidence indicates that the DNA chain is unbranched and measurements of the physical properties such as sedimentation, diffusion, light scattering and viscosity indicate that DNA is an asymmetric molecule about 20 Angstroms wide and very long (about 3×10^4 nucleotides). The surprising thing about this long, thin molecule is that it is relatively rigid, a property which is not expected for a polymer of these dimensions. Studies of the pattern obtained after x-ray crystallography showed that two structures could exist—the exact form depended on the degree of hydration. The general appearance of the x-ray pattern suggested a helical structure. It might be recalled that immediately preceding the appearance of the Watson-Crick structure Pauling and his group had shown that the helix was the basis for the structure of the fibrous protein molecules. Crystallography permits calculation of the unit cell of DNA and these data along with the measured density led to the conclusion that there must be *two* nucleotide chains in each crystal unit. The titration curves of DNA suggested that hydrogen bond formation was an important element in the structure. (The hydrogen bond is a weak bond connecting hydrogen with two electronegative atoms such as two oxygens or with an oxygen and nitrogen atom.)

In the proposed structure as described by Watson and Crick (1953c), two polynucleotide chains are coiled around a common axis to form a helix (Fig. 10). The two chains are joined together by hydrogen bonds between the nucleotide bases. The phosphates and sugar groups are on the outside of the helix; the bases are on the inside. The distance from the axis of the helix to the phosphorus atoms on the outside is ten Angstroms. The unique feature of the structure rests on the arrangement of the bases. These are arranged perpendicular to the fiber axis and are joined together in specific pairs. The structure will only fit together in the necessary dimensions if adenine pairs specifically with thymine while guanine pairs specifically with cytosine (or the substituted cytosines, methyl cytosine or hydroxymethyl cytosine) (Fig. 11). This necessity for specific pairing is the unique and unexpected feature of the structure. There is no known restriction on the sequence of bases in one chain but it is obvious that the chains are complementary; that is, once the sequence of bases in one chain is known, the necessity for specific pairing determines the sequence of bases in the second chain. It is this feature of complementarity that makes the structure of great interest to biologists.

One of the basic questions of biology, perhaps *the* basic question, is how do organisms duplicate themselves? The question is so important that it is almost as important to know that a satisfactory

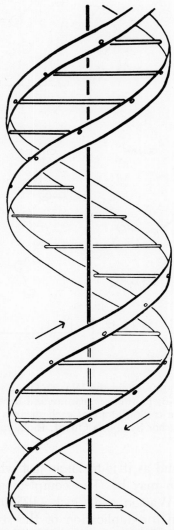

Figure 10. The Watson-Crick structure of DNA. The figure is diagrammatic. The two ribbons symbolize the two phosphate-sugar chains and the horizontal rods indicate the paths of bases holding the chains together. The vertical line marks the fiber axis. (Watson and Crick, Cold Spring Harbor Symposia Quant. Biol., vol. 18, 1953.)

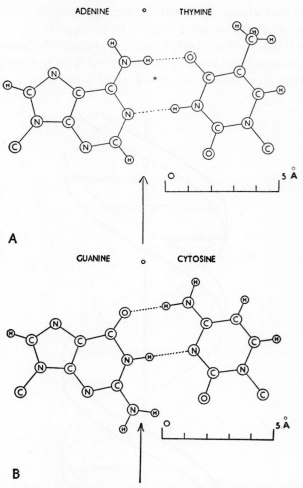

Figure 11. Pairing of bases in the Watson-Crick structure. A, Pairing of adenine and thymine. B, Pairing of guanine and cytosine. Hydrogen bonds are shown dotted. One carbon atom of each sugar is shown. (Watson and Crick, Cold Spring Harbor Symposia Quant. Biol., vol. 18, 1953.)

solution can be found as it is to know just what the "true" solution of the problem may be. The complementary nature of the DNA structure of Watson and Crick (1953b) immediately suggested a mechanism for duplication of the structure. If the two chains were to separate and if each were to attract a complement of itself the net result of the process would be duplication. One of the major problems with this idea is that it would be necessary to unwind a highly coiled structure. Calculations indicate that the energy requirement for such an uncoiling is not too great (Levinthal and Crane 1956). Nonetheless a detailed model for the duplication of the coiled DNA as it occurs *in vivo* is difficult to make even though there have been several attempts (Stent 1958).

The linearity of the DNA structure and the non-determined sequence of bases fit the genetic requirements for a molecule determining hereditary characteristics since the structure itself seems to suggest that the genetic information is contained in the base sequence which forms a linear code. This idea in turn suggests that mutation represents a mistake in the duplication of the base order: If ATGCCCGTACA represents a genetic message, then a mistake in duplication to give AGTCCC . . . . might represent a mutation (see below, Chapter 4).

Some time ago it would have been possible to write that the double stranded DNA structure occurs in all organisms. Very recently there have been reports of a virus which has a single stranded DNA structure, judged from its susceptibility to inactivation by P-32 decay (an efficiency of one inactivation per disintegration which is about ten times greater than the efficiency of inactivation of the double stranded phage DNA) and by the queer physical properties of the nucleic acid (Sinsheimer 1959, Tessman 1959). It will be extremely interesting to see how the DNA in this virus is duplicated and to study the mutability of the strain.

The finding of a virus with a single stranded DNA implies that the genetic information can be contained in a single strand. This supposition is confirmed by the experiments of Marmur and Lane (1960). Double stranded DNA will split into two halves upon heating; the separated strands can recombine under the proper conditions. Transforming principle is inactivated by heat, presumably because of this separation. Marmur and Lane heat inactivated transforming principle containing a mutant marker. Incubation of this heat treated, transforming principle with homologous wild type DNA (heat treated) restored transforming activity for the mutant marker. Physical studies by Doty *et al.* (1960) using N-15 labeled material (*cf* below) showed that this treatment resulted in the formation of hybrid DNA containing two strands of different origin, one from the mutant and one from the wild type. Since this hybrid DNA produced transformation for the mutant marker, the experiments indicate that a single DNA strand can carry the information needed for transformation.

VI. *The Synthesis of DNA*

One of the really surprising developments (to biologists) of the past few years has been the description by Kornberg (1957) and his colleagues of an enzyme system which synthesizes DNA. The synthesis is detected by the incorporation of labeled deoxyribonucleotides into DNA using an enzyme preparation obtained from cells of *E. coli* in the logarithmic phase of growth. A net synthesis of 50 per cent or better has been reported. The enzyme system has the following characteristics: All four deoxyribonucleotide *tri*phosphates are required for appreciable synthesis (the diphosphates will not substitute), magnesium ion is required, the system is essentially irreversible (as would be required to explain the metabolic stability of DNA) and about 1 per cent of the maximum reaction rate is obtained when a single nucleotide is eliminated from the reaction mixture. Polymerized DNA is required to serve as a "primer" for the reaction, perhaps to provide the template upon which complementary chains are constructed. The activity of the primer is increased by heating, indicating that it is a single strand of DNA which serves as a model. The enzyme constructs real DNA since the bases are incorporated in the ratios required by the Watson-Crick structure (Lehman *et al.* 1958) and are not incorporated in ratios determined by their concentration in the reaction mixture as is the case for the polynucleotide phosphorylase described by Ochoa (Ochoa and Heppel 1957) which synthesizes *an* RNA. In some ways these findings raise more questions than they answer (hence their stimulating effect) because we have no idea of the relationship between this enzyme system and DNA synthesis in organisms. In cells of higher organisms DNA synthesis is restricted to the interphase period in which the chromosomes are still in their extended form and are not easily visible. Studies using the autoradiograph method indicate that DNA synthesis occurs during the middle of the interphase period (Howard and Pelc 1951, Taylor 1957). There must be some sort of biological "signal" to set DNA synthesis going since this synthesis is not a continuous activity of the cell in higher organisms. Presumably the synthesis of DNA requires the activation of the Kornberg enzyme but we have no idea what sort of signal is required.

VII. *The Distribution of DNA to Progeny*

If the Watson-Crick structure is correct then a method for following the individual strands should show that after the first duplication the material is conserved, that is, if the strands contain
isotope the activity of particular strands will not be further diluted
(Fig. 12) (Perutz 1958). Consider a labeled DNA molecule in
which both strands are labeled and call the specific activity of the
whole strand two. Then if duplication occurs in non-labeled medium each of the daughter molecules will have one parental,
labeled strand and one new, unlabeled strand giving a specific
activity for the molecule as a whole of one. On further duplication
two types of molecules are possible. In one, an unlabeled strand
serves as a parent; this gives a second generation daughter molecule
with an activity of zero. If a labeled strand serves as a complement,
that daughter molecule will still have a specific activity of one; after
the first dilution there can be no change in the specific activity
of any daughter molecule that happens to be labeled—if the
Watson-Crick hypothesis adequately describes what happens in
living cells.

An elegant method to test this hypothesis with the bacterium
E. coli has been developed by Messelson and Stahl (1958) using
the technique of density gradient ultracentrifugation. It is possible

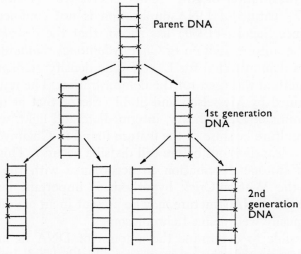

Parent DNA

1st generation
DNA

2nd
generation
DNA

Figure 12. Distribution of isotopic label of parent DNA among double
helices of progeny DNA. The crosses indicate isotopic markers. (Perutz,
Endeavour, vol. 17, 1958.)

to separate molecules of DNA enriched with N-15 from those containing mainly N-14 by this method, which employs ultracentrifugation in a medium whose density varies continuously because of the concentration gradient which occurs when solutions of salts such as $CsCl_2$ are centrifuged at high speed. The equilibrium position of a molecule in the ultracentrifuge depends both on the density of the suspending medium and on the sedimentation constant of the molecule and this method makes it possible to separate molecules differing only slightly in density. In this experiment bacteria were grown in N-15 labeled medium; the cells were then removed from the medium and a portion were incubated for a known average number of divisions in medium containing a nitrogen source that was not enriched with the stable isotope N-15. The DNA was isolated and its sedimentation pattern was determined. The results of the experiment were perfectly clear. After the first division in non-labeled medium the DNA obtained was homogeneous and had a molecular weight intermediate between N-15 labeled and non-labeled DNA. After the second and subsequent divisions two DNA molecular species were observed; one was of intermediate molecular weight and the other had the normal (*i.e.*, non-labeled) molecular weight. The proportion of molecules of intermediate molecular weight diminished as division proceeded as required by the Watson-Crick hypothesis.

The demonstration of this "semi-conservative" (Delbruck and Stent 1957) nature of DNA duplication is not confined to the bacteria since Sueoka (1960) has shown that the distribution of DNA in the mitotic division of *Chlamydomonas reinhardi* follows the pattern demonstrated for *E. coli*. The density gradient centrifugation method was used for the demonstration. The results were those obtained by Messelson and Stahl (except that at one stage all three forms of DNA, heavy, intermediate and light, were present in the culture because of the feature found in Chlamydomonas of many nuclear divisions before cell division occurs). This demonstration of isotope distribution in accordance with the requirements of the Watson-Crick hypothesis is important because it shows that this DNA structure may be present in an organism with morphologically well defined chromosomes.

It is possible to determine the amount of DNA in individual bacteriophage particles by preparing virus highly labeled with P-32 and then imbedding the phage in a photographic emulsion of the type used in cosmic ray studies (Levinthal 1956, Thomas 1959).

Decay of the P-32 results in the emission of beta particles into the emulsion and the passage of the beta particles results in a track of silver granules in the emulsion. The phage behaves as a point source and successive phosphorus disintegrations in the same virus particle result in the formation of a star shaped figure. Counting the number of tracks per star yields information on the average number of P-32 atoms per source and the variation of the number of phosphorus atoms from source to source. Data obtained by this method indicate that the phage particle contains two types of DNA. After osmotic shock 0.4 of the phage phosphorus remains together as a single large piece while the remainder of the DNA does not produce stars and is presumably dispersed as small pieces. First generation progeny phage produced from labeled parents contain a few phage particles which contain about 0.2 of the parental DNA. This phosphorus (in the daughter phage) does not disperse on osmotic shock. Finally, if the daughter phage particles are passed through a second growth cycle the large DNA fragments (containing 0.2 of the original label) do not diminish in size or number in the offspring. This type of experiment indicates that the large DNA piece is distributed and duplicated according to the Watson-Crick model.

As mentioned before, bacteriophage particles containing radiophosphorus, P-32, die off at a rate which is proportional to the number of radioactive atoms they contain. This death results from the P-32 $\rightarrow$ S-32 transmutation and is not caused by the beta radiation accompanying the isotope decay. The P-32 decay apparently leads to the disintegration of the DNA molecule in which it is located. However the offspring of highly radioactive phages are stable; that is, they are not killed by P-32 decay at the rate that would be expected if the P-32 transferred from parent to daughter was uniformly distributed throughout the progeny. This implies that the parental P-32 which is transferred must be concentrated in a very few of the infective progeny particles produced per infective center. It is possible to test this idea by studying the ability of phages to transfer their P-32 to subsequent generations after storage of the particles long enough to allow for phage inactivation caused by the radioactive decay (Stent, Sato and Jerne 1959). Only viable virus particles will be able to transfer material to progeny. Determination of the transferability of the P-32 permits calculation of the rate of loss of viability which in turn permits calculation of the phosphorus content of the inactivated phage, since the rate of loss of viability is proportional to the amount of incorporated radioactive phosphorus. The results of this type of experiment do differ in detail from the results obtained by the use of the technique of star production described above. There are features in both types of experiment, however, that definitely support the idea that the Watson-Crick structure exists in the bacteriophage. First, the transferred P-32 is concentrated, in part, in a very few phage particles and secondly, the DNA in progeny particles which originates from parental DNA is not subject to further dilution on continued replication. This is a requirement if reproduction follows the scheme indicated by the Watson-Crick structure.

The experiments discussed so far have all been done with microorganisms in which (with the exception of Chlamydomonas) the complex morphological chromosomes found in the higher organisms have not been demonstrated. It has been possible to follow the distribution of DNA in the root tips of a higher plant using the method of autoradiography (Taylor, Wood and Hughes 1957). Three technical details make it possible to do experiments of this type. The first is the use of radioactive tritium as a label in studies by the autoradiographic technique. In this technique a photographic film is placed over a biological preparation and the location of the isotope, even within cells, can be detected by the formation of silver granules in the film as a result of the beta radiation produced on isotope decay. The resolution of the method depends on the range of the beta particles. Carbon-14 gives rather poor resolution because it emits beta particles with a large enough range to make their exact point of origin uncertain. The range of the beta particles from tritium, H^3, is so low that the silver granules are formed immediately over the point at which isotope decay is located. Secondly, thymidine is used as a "selective and specific" label for DNA. When this substance is fed to rapidly dividing cells it is almost immediately incorporated into the DNA—and nowhere else—and it remains in the DNA with a very low turnover because of the metabolic stability of this polymer. Thirdly, colchicine is used to block cell division without disturbing chromosome duplication. The ploidy (number of chromosome sets) is therefore a measure of the number of chromosome divisions since addition of the colchicine. The introduction of the colchicine into the experiment may have other consequences. Effects of colchicine on DNA formation have been reported (La Cour and Pelc 1958, 1959).

Taylor's experiment was performed as follows: seedlings of *Vicia faba* were grown for one root cell division in solutions containing tritium labeled thymidine. The thymidine was removed and growth was continued in medium without isotope but with colchicine. At intervals the distribution of label in the chromosomes was determined by autoradiography. Mitotic division was studied in all cases. The results of this experiment are those that would be expected on the basis of the Watson-Crick model (Fig. 13). After removal of the isotope, but before division in the absence of isotope, all the chromosomes are equally labeled. After one division in the absence of isotope these labeled chromosomes produce a labeled and a non-labeled chromosome—except where sister chromatid exchange (somatic crossing over) has occurred in which case complementary portions are labeled. After two divisions about one-quarter of the chromosomes are labeled; there is no further dilution of labeled units. The mode of isotope distribution is therefore semi-conservative and is that required by the Watson-Crick model.

The results appear to be easily interpreted on the basis of the model but it is difficult to conceive that plant chromosomes are simply highly coiled single Watson-Crick double helices. In Lilium the amount of DNA per haploid chromosome set is 53×10^{-12} gm. If this were made into a single double-helix the helix would be 1.5×10^7 microns or 15 meters long and have 4.4×10^9 coils (Taylor 1957). Since there are 12 chromosomes, the length per chromosome of the helix would be about 1½ meters. Chromo-

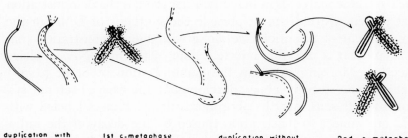

duplication with   1st c-metaphase   duplication without   2nd c-metaphase
labeled thymidine   after labeling   labeled thymidine   after labeling

Figure 13. Results and interpretation of Taylor's results with tritium labeled thymidine. Diagrammatic representation of proposed organization and mode of replication which would produce the result seen in the autoradiographs. The two units necessary to explain the results are shown, although these were not resolved by microscopic examination. Solid lines represent non-labeled units while those in dashed lines are labeled. The dots represent grains in the autoradiographs. (Taylor, American Naturalist, vol. 91, 1957.)

somes are highly complex organelles containing protein, RNA and other substances and the morpohological integrity of the structure is not exclusively determined by the DNA. It may be necessary to consider other models of the chromosome; for example, Taylor has considered a model in which many Watson-Crick helices are attached at right angles to a central protein core. Studies with the hydrolytic enzymes indicate that the chromosome structure may be held together by protein. Plaut and Mazia (1956) have reported experiments using labeled thymidine in which a regular distribution of activity was not obtained; LaCour and Pelc (1958, 1959) have also obtained results which appear to differ from those of Taylor. The design of these experiments was different from Taylor's experiment. The coincidence between Taylor's results and the results of Sueoka (1960) on Chlamydomonas makes interpretation in terms of the Watson-Crick structure easiest.

In microorganisms the evidence seems quite reasonable that the DNA is distributed as required by the Watson-Crick structure and, again, evidence obtained from studies with the microorganisms certainly establishes the fact that DNA can carry genetic information. It is an easy and I think reasonable extrapolation to suppose that DNA is the *only* substance that can carry genetic information in organisms which contain this substance. It must be clearly understood that *this is an extrapolation and not yet unequivocably established.* In fact it seems likely to me that more attention will be given to the role of protein and of RNA in the transfer of information. There are several lines of evidence that indicate the importance of these materials in heredity. First there is the demonstration that protein synthesis must precede the synthesis of DNA in the development of bacteriophage along with the demonstration that some protein is probably injected along with the DNA in phage infection. More important is the demonstration by Stent (1955) that at some stage in phage development the phage-bacterial system loses its sensitivity to phosphorus decay. Phages labeled with P-32 are subject to inactivation caused by the decay of the radioisotope. Phosphorus labeled bacteria are also subject to inactivation by isotope decay. If labeled bacteria are infected with labeled phages and development of the phages is allowed to continue for a short time before the system is frozen and stored (to permit isotope decay), it is found that the phage particles are no longer subject to inactivation by decay; that is, when the system is thawed phage development will proceed essentially as if isotope decay has not occurred. This finding implies a transfer of the genetic information of the phage to some non-phosphorus containing molecule, that is to something other than DNA. It is conceivable that some molecule, not nucleic acid, protects the phage DNA from the disintegrating effects of decay. Stent (1958) has suggested that an RNA protein might be formed as a third chain along the DNA double helix, that this might be more resistant to P-32 decay than the DNA and that the ribonucleoprotein might then serve as a model for the formation of a new DNA double helix. The RNA of tobacco mosaic virus certainly does carry genetic information.

Notwithstanding these possibilities, the point remains that DNA, free from any other substance, can transfer linked hereditary information. The idea that this information is encoded in the sequence of the DNA bases will be discussed in the next chapter.

Chapter Three

The Molecular Meaning of

Genetic Recombination

"The theory states that the characters of the individual are referable to paired elements (genes) in the germinal material that are held together in a definite number of linkage groups; it states that the members of each pair of genes separate when the germ cells mature in accordance with Mendel's first law, and in consequence each germ cell comes to contain one set only; it states that the members belonging to different linkage groups assort independently in accordance with Mendel's second law; it states that an orderly interchange—crossing over—also takes place at times between the elements in corresponding linkage groups; and it states that the frequency of crossing over furnishes evidence of the linear order of the elements in each linkage group and of the relative position of the elements with respect to each other."

from T. H. Morgan, "The Theory of the Gene," 1926

Linkage and recombination studies have probably been the items of major interest in the development of genetics. Many geneticists have been much more interested in the problems of gene transmission than in the problems of gene action or gene mutation. In part this is because it is difficult even today to design meaningful experiments on the problems of gene action. For

61

example, what sort of experiment will decide just *how* genes determine amino acid sequences in peptides? More important, studies of how genes are linked together and of how the combinations of genes are changed are the operational tools for defining the gene. Obviously the problem of a satisfactory, operational definition of the gene is a central one for the study of heredity.

I. *The Principles of Genetics*

It is easiest to summarize the principles of genetics using a haploid organism as an example. Most of the plants and animals with which we are familiar contain two complete sets of chromosomes in their cells (*i.e.*, are *diploid*) but certain of the "lower" forms such as the fungi contain only one set and are termed *monoploid* or more commonly *haploid*. All genes are expressed immediately in organisms having but one set of chromosomes (in the absence of special sorts of gene interaction, *i.e.*, suppressor action) since there is no second set of genes to create problems of dominance. When two alternate forms of a gene are present in a diploid organism, the organism may display a character (or *phenotype*) characteristic of one of the genes rather than some intermediate character. We call such a gene *dominant* in contrast to the *recessive* gene which is not expressed.

Diploid organisms with two different forms of a gene are called *heterozygotes*, those with two identical representatives are *homozygotes* and they may be homozygous recessive or homozygous dominant. In cases where there is dominance we say that the heterozygote has the phenotype of the dominant gene and that only the homozygous recessive has the phenotype characteristic of the recessive gene or recessive allele. Alternate forms of the same gene are termed *alleles*. Furthermore we distinguish between the phenotype—what the organism looks like—and the *genotype*, the genetic constitution which may or may not be phenotypically expressed. In haploid organisms the genotype is necessarily expressed (with the exception noted above) and it is simple to classify this type of organism when genetic or breeding experiments are performed.

The quotation marks around the term "lower organisms" to describe the haploid forms are seriously intended. All of the organisms now present on the earth have had an equally long evolutionary history. It seems presumptuous to classify them as higher or lower based on their resemblance to the most familiar things we know. Study of some of the life cycles of the fungi, for example, indicates how complex they are. On the other hand, it is convenient to use the terms "higher" and "lower" and they will be used in the usual intuitive sense.

The sexual spores or ascospores of *Neurospora crassa* (Chapter 1) are genetically haploid. Suppose we have a strain carrying two mutant genes designated *a* and *b*; the normal, or wild type form of these genes will be designated +. The use of the term wild type is common in genetics but it has no real meaning other than to designate the form considered as standard in the strain studied in the laboratory. There are often many different alleles of the same gene present in natural populations and in some cases it would be difficult to decide which represented the wild type and which the mutant type. If we cross the double mutant strain of Neurospora *ab* to the wild type ++, four possible types of offspring may be obtained. There are the types *ab* and ++ which are the *parental* types and the types *a*+ and +*b* in which there has been a reassortment of the characters. These are the *recombinant* types. Often it is found that there are statistically equal numbers of each of the four types; that is 25 per cent of the progeny are *ab*, 25 per cent are +*b* and so on. This is the result to be expected according to the Mendelian laws applied to a haploid organism.

Occasionally in the cross *ab* × ++ results of the following type are obtained:

parental types	⟨ *a* *b*	45 per cent
	+ +	45 per cent
recombinant types	⟨ *a* +	5 per cent
	+ *b*	5 per cent

That is, in some crosses there is a great excess of parental types but some recombinant types are obtained. Now this is a result which is very common in genetics and it was explained successfully so early in the history of the science that I think that many geneticists have lost their ability to wonder at what it really does mean on a molecular basis. One of the facts that must be emphasized is that both types of recombinants are obtained in equal numbers, or as we say the *reciprocal recombinants* are always obtained. It seems very likely that in organisms with definite chromosomes in the cytological sense, if the recombinant *a*+ is formed by crossing over, then the reciprocal recombinant +*b* is formed at the same time and in the same event. It is a feature of modern science that even though genetics is only about sixty years old this type of recombination is already called "classical recombination."

A great deal of experimentation has shown that genes *a* and *b* in the above example are physically connected or *linked* on the same chromosome. The formation of the relatively small proportion of recombinant types from crosses involving linked genes takes place by a process called *crossing over*. In corn, Drosophila and presumably in other organisms having definite, visible chromosomes (like Neurospora or Chlamydomonas) there is a definite physical exchange of chromosomal material accompanying genetic recombination or crossing over. It is possible to prepare mutant stocks of corn and Drosophila with definite morphological chromosome abnormalities as well as with mutant genes. Recombination of the genetic characteristics is perfectly correlated with recombination of the morphological chromosomal abnormalities, indicating that a physical exchange has taken place.

In Neurospora and in other organisms two haploid gametes fuse to form a diploid zygote. In the higher organisms the somatic cells, the organism as we know it, are derived from the diploid zygote cell. In the formation of the sex cells in higher organisms and immediately after formation of the zygote in Neurospora there occurs a process of reduction division or *meiosis* in which the chromosome number is reduced from the diploid to the haploid number (Fig. 14). Crossing over is supposed to occur during this process. The chromosomes pair in a peculiar manner so that homologous chromosomes come to lie in exact apposition. This process of *synapsis* is extremely exact but the chemical basis for the perfect attraction of homologous parts is completely unknown. The chromosomes are seen to exist as four strands (two from each member of the chromosome pair) but the exact time of their division is not definitely known; then they separate as cell division occurs. A second cell division follows without chromosome duplication. This division results in cells which contain the haploid number of chromosomes. Crossing over takes place at the four strand stage of chromosome division; presumably each chromosome is divided into two strands and the four strands occur together in synapsis.

The simplest proof of this idea is obtained by study of the segregation of mutant genes in Neurospora. In contrast to the situation with higher organisms all of the products of meiosis are recovered in this organism. In female Drosophila the process of meiosis results in four nuclei, each containing a haploid set of chromosomes. Three of the four nuclei never appear in progeny since they degenerate in the polar bodies. The results of genetic experimentation with Drosophila represent an average result. With Neurospora each chromosome set is included in a nucleus which forms a viable ascospore. (Actually there is a mitotic division following the process of meiosis to give eight nuclei and eight ascospores but this has no effect on the genetic picture.) The ascospores are arranged in a definite order; isolation of the spores in

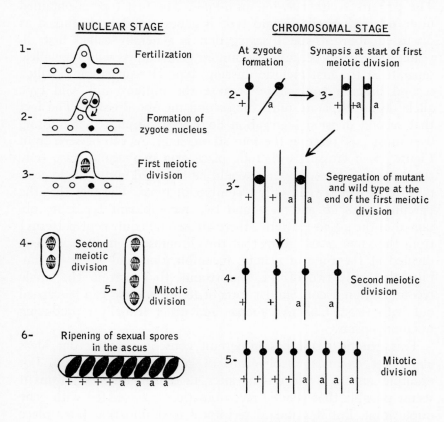

Figure 14. Nuclear and chromosomal basis of genetic segregation in *Neurospora crassa.* The solid circles on the left indicate the nuclei coming from one parent, open circles indicate nuclei coming from the second parent. Solid circles on the right indicate the position of the centromere. Only one chromosomal pair of the seven in this species is followed.

order followed by germination will give eight cultures which yield information on the order in which events occur during meiosis. (Since spore pairs are identical the results will be presented for simplicity as though there were only four spores.)

If we make the cross $ab \times ++$ and isolate the progeny spores in order, two types of results are obtained (Fig. 15). Considering the segregation of gene a these results are:

> Type I a (b) : a (b) : $+$ $(+)$: $+$ $(+)$ and
> Type II a (b) : $+$ (b) : a $(+)$: $+$ $(+)$.

The pattern is either $aa++$ or $a+a+$. The first type is obtained more often than the second type if genes a and b are linked as discussed above. Type I segregation is generally called first division segregation because the mutant gene and its wild type allele separate at the first meiotic division; type II segregation is called second division segregation because the mutant and wild type allele do not separate until the second meiotic division. The fact that second division segregation does occur implies that crossing over must take place in the four strand stage. As can be seen from Figure 15, if crossing over took place at a two strand stage only the patterns $aa++$ or $++aa$ could be obtained and a single cross over event would yield only recombinant types. The fact that the parental types ab and $++$ and two recombinant types are obtained in the $a+a+$ pattern (there are several equivalent patterns) from the same ascus means that the chromosome must have been divided at the time of genetic recombination and it further implies that only two of the four strands took part in the single recombination event. Similar sorts of *tetrad analysis* can be carried out with yeast, Chlamydomonas and other sexually reproducing microorganisms.

This genetic result has important consequences for our ideas about the chemical mechanisms of genetic recombination. For example, and as I will discuss later, in certain microorganisms it seems possible that genetic recombination is associated with gene duplication. But if standard reciprocal recombination takes place in the four strand stage after the chromosomes become visibly split and paired, as is generally believed, classical recombination must occur after DNA reproduction has taken place and recombination therefore is not related to gene duplication. It has been demonstrated that DNA reproduction occurs during the interphase period before the chromosomes become visible and paired (Howard and Pelc 1951).

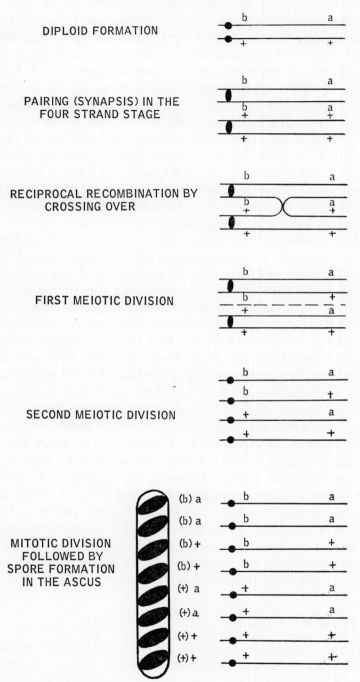

Figure 15. Diagrammatic representation of second division segregation in *Neurospora crassa.*

With certain exceptions the recombination frequencies (that is, the fraction of recombinant types) obtained by crossing different linked genes are approximately additive. For example, if in the cross *ab* × ++ there is 5 per cent recombination and in the cross *bc* × ++ there is 5 per cent recombination, then in the cross *ac* × ++ there will be 10 per cent recombination (or 0 per cent recombination if *a* and *c* are alleles or "alternate forms of the same gene," that is, occupy similar positions on homologous chromosomes). This additivity of recombination frequencies led to the idea that the genes are connected together in a linear array on the chromosomes. Genetic maps have been constructed based on the idea that the frequency with which two genes recombined could be used as a measure of the distance between them.

Most geneticists have thought of the process of recombination as requiring that two homologous chromosomes split at homologous locations and that there is a rejoining of the chromosome fragments with a recombination of partners in the process. (It is this idea which shocks my friends in the other sciences.) Regardless of the mechanisms, experiments with many different organisms are *all* consistent with the idea that the genetic material is arranged in a linear or unidimensional order. This idea of the linearity of the genetic material is fundamental and any hypothesis of the chemical nature of the hereditary material must take it into account. Taylor's first (1957) proposed structure for the chromosome, with DNA strands coming out from a central protein backbone, required modification to a hypothesis in which the DNA strands were also connected with one another to form a linear sequence (Taylor 1958). Although the genetic order is always that obtained from mapping studies there is no necessary correlation (in Drosophila) between physical distance and map distance. That is, a map unit at one portion of the chromosome may have a different physical (or cytological) length from a map unit at another portion of the chromosome even though the order of the genes is that indicated by genetic studies.*

II. What Is a Gene?

The preoccupation of geneticists with linkage and recombination studies seems strange at first to the biochemist. He can intui-

* For further information on the fundamental principles of genetics one of the many standard works should be consulted.

tively understand the rationale of investigations on the gene-enzyme relationship but he often finds it difficult to understand the emphasis on recombination in genetics. However, such studies are a most elegant method of investigating the nature of the gene itself. In order to establish a definitive relationship between genes and enzymes we must certainly know what both these entities are. We now know (since Sanger's work) what a protein is and we are quite certain that we know what an enzyme is. Actually as Green and Järnefelt (1959) point out and as I have mentioned earlier we may only know what the class of soluble enzymes is really like; complexes of enzymes structurally organized on biological particles may represent structures that make it impossible to define just what a single enzyme is. Similarly, it is not quite so simple to decide just what a single gene is, that is, to limit the boundaries of a single gene within a linkage group. In fact, Goldschmidt (1955) often suggested that the concept of an individual gene is only an abstraction and that attention must be centered on whole linkage groups.

Classical genetics had two main operational techniques for defining the gene. Suppose that in a haploid organism two genes, m_1 and m_2 both affect the same phenotype; for example, suppose that both these genes when they occur separately lead to a nutritional requirement for the amino acid methionine. If the two genes are different then the cross m_1 $(+)$ $\times$ $(+)$ m_2 should yield wild type organisms $++$ as a result of recombination and in addition the double mutant m_1m_2 should be obtained. Obviously the same test is applicable to diploid organisms but it is slightly more complex because of the problems of dominance. Genes m_1 and m_2 are presumed to be different if wild types are obtained as a result of crossing strains carrying the genes. This is the classical test for allelism. Two genes are allelic (at identical loci) if wild types are not obtained from such a cross. The definition assumes that recombination does not occur within genes; the genes are visualized as strung out on a chromosome string and recombination is assumed to occur between the gene "beads" on the string but not within the beads. It is also obvious that this definition of the gene depends on the number of progeny that can be scored; if two genes are close enough together in a linkage group so that recombination between them occurs only rarely, they will be considered the same gene in an organism whose progeny are difficult to classify but will be considered different genes in an organism whose progeny

69

are easily classified. A gene in a bacterial virus in which millions of progeny are easily scored is therefore a different entity from a gene in man where even a few pedigrees are difficult to obtain.

The gene may also be defined as a unit of function. Biochemically, two genes are obviously different if they lead to a requirement for different nutritional supplements or if they affect the production or activity of different enzymes. This type of test of unitary function is not really adequate because we still do not know enough biochemistry to be able to recognize all the intermediates or to be able to isolate all the enzymes. There is a genetic test for unity of function which is possible if the genes involved are both recessive in the single mutant condition. If a diploid heterozygote m_1 $(+)$ $/\!/$ $(+)$ m_2 is wild type then m_1 and m_2 must be functionally different; if the diploid is mutant in phenotype we conclude that m_1 and m_2 affect the same function. Obviously the test will work only if the heterozygotes $+/\!/m_1$ and $+/\!/m_2$ are both wild type in phenotype. The experiment can also be done with haploid organisms which form heterocaryons since the arrangement m_1+ in one nucleus and $+m_2$ in the other is analogous in many ways to the situation in diploids where both representatives are present in one nucleus on homologous chromosomes.

It can be seen rather quickly that there are real difficulties with this functional test. It will be recalled that mutants of Neurospora deficient in the single enzyme adenylsuccinase, or the single enzyme glutamic dehydrogenase, nonetheless complement each other: that is, form heterocaryons which will grow on minimal medium and produce enzyme. Two functional tests therefore give different answers. The situation is really even more complicated since the heterocaryons which are formed by complementation only approach the wild type phenotype—only about 25 per cent of the normal amount of enzyme is produced. Other cases have been reported in which the *trans* configuration (Chapter 1) gives an organism of intermediate phenotype.

If m_1 and m_2 are functional alleles affecting the same character then the *cis* configuration, with the two mutant alleles on the same chromosome and the two wild type alleles on the second chromosome (that is, $m_1m_2/\!/++$), will be wild type since it is completely analogous to the condition $m/\!/+$ where m is a recessive gene. In classical genetics, once it was concluded that m_1 and m_2 were alleles the configuration m_1m_2 on the same chromosome would have no meaning (except in the rare case of a gene duplication or of unequal crossing over) since such a combination could be obtained only by the recombination of alleles (that is, of the impenetrable beads on the chromosome string) which was judged to be impossible. This configuration $(m_1m_2/\!/++)$ of functional alleles *can* be obtained and its existence is the basis for the phenomenon of pseudoallelism. We can therefore define a gene in the functional sense as "that part of a chromosome within which recessive mutants behave as allelic to one another, that is, determine a mutant phenotype when in combinations of two in *trans* but not when in *cis*." The gene defined in this way was first called a "section" by Pontecorvo and Roper (1956) and a *cistron* by Benzer (1957); the cistron terminology is being used more widely (Pontecorvo 1958).

Two different definitions of the gene have been suggested so far, each based on definite operations. We can also define a gene as a unit of mutation (the smallest element of the genetic material that, when altered, can give rise to a mutant form of the organism), but the operations involved make this method unsuitable for routine use. The definition of the gene on the basis of recombination and on the basis of function presumably define the same entity and we should expect that both methods should coincide, that is, should give the same answer as to whether or not two genes are alleles. Actually there are many cases now known in which the two methods give different answers. One of the earliest cases was recognized as a result of the investigation of the lozenge mutants of Drosophila (Green and Green 1949). Two recessive mutants of this series of mutants, lz^{46} and lz^g are 0.06 recombination (map) units apart. They are therefore different genes. However, $lz^{46} +/\!/ + lz^g$ flies are definitely mutant in phenotype although $lz^{46}lz^g/\!/++$ flies are normal. The genes are therefore the same, *i.e.*, a single gene. This paradox is known as position pseudoallelism or the "Lewis Effect" (Pontecorvo 1958) and it points up a fundamental ambiguity in the definitions of the gene we have adopted; they do not give the same answer.

Pontecorvo (1956) has given a very pretty illustration showing how the distinction between different genes becomes less sharp as the genes get closer together. Pontecorvo and his group have been studying *Aspergillus nidulans,* a fungus which forms diploids and undergoes mitotic recombination. The mutants *w* (white), *pro* (proline-requiring) and *ribo* (riboflavin-requiring) are all

71

linked together but they are far apart on the recombination map and are easily separated functionally. There is no difficulty in identifying them as separate genes. The recessive adenine-requiring mutants *ad-14*, *ad-9* and *ad-8* are also located far apart on the same chromosome. This means that crosses between them give many wild type recombinants. The three mutants give growth responses to the same compounds (but only a limited number of intermediates in the series were known or available at the time of the tests) but are functionally different as determined by the *cis-trans* test in both diploid heterozygotes and heterocaryons. These then are also obviously different genes.

The three adenine-requiring mutants *ad-23*, *ad-1* and *ad-3* are very closely linked but they can be distinguished by the *cis-trans* test for complementarity. The two mutants *ad-1* and *ad-3* recombine at a frequency of 10^{-3} which means that about 10,000 products of meiosis must be analyzed to detect the recombinants. These are different genes by both tests but in an organism like Drosophila it would not have been likely that enough progeny would be classified to detect the recombinants.

Finally, Pontecorvo considers the "recurrences" of mutation at the *ad-8* locus, particularly those mutants designated *ad-8*, *ad-11*, *ad-16* and *ad-20*. All these mutations are at approximately the same position on the chromosome and all are indistinguishable by the *cis-trans* test of complementarity. Some growth of *ad-20* and *ad-16* occurs in the absence of adenine and a series of suppressors located at different positions suppress *ad-20* (but none of the other alleles) in a manner similar to the suppressors of the *td* locus in Neurospora. In spite of their functional identity the genes can be arranged in a linear order based on recombination. The total length of the unit is about 0.3 per cent recombination and *ad-20* and *ad-16* show the extremely low recombination frequency of 10^{-6}. In some cases at least this recombination is classical reciprocal recombination by crossing over, since the double mutant has been recovered in the *cis* configuration by mitotic crossing over from the *trans*. Pontecorvo has stated that up to the time of his writing (1956) it had not been possible to find a mutant which failed to recombine with a recurrence.

III. *The Size of the Gene*

Part of the difficulty in defining the gene is the acceptance of certain assumptions. If we assume that there is no recombination within genes then the units of function will almost always be multiple. It is probably a simpler idea to admit that recombination can occur within genes. A *gene, or a cistron, is a unit of function and consists of many parts.* The recombining unit within a gene can be called a *recon* (Benzer 1957) and the *muton* can be defined as the smallest element which when altered gives a mutant form of the organism. The next problem is to estimate the size of the various units we have adopted. Since we now assume that the linear genetic material is DNA and that it is the sequence of nucleotides which carries the genetic information, it is amusing to estimate the size of the cistron, muton and recon in terms of nucleotides, or, since the nucleotides occur paired in the Watson-Crick structure, in terms of nucleotide pairs.

What is needed to estimate these units is a method that will detect recombinants even when they occur at an extremely low frequency. We would like to find out what is the lowest recombination rate possible. This problem was first studied by Benzer (*l.c.*) using the rII mutants of bacteriophages. Wild type bacteriophages form plaques on both strains B and K of *Escherichia coli*. The rII mutants form plaques only on strain B. The mutants have an altered plaque morphology on strain B which permits their recognition. Strain B of *E. coli* is infected with a mixture of two rII mutants. The phage/bacteria ratio is arranged so that on the average each bacterium is infected by both types of phage. The bacteria are allowed to lyse and the lysate is then plated on both strains B and K. If plaques appear on strain K it is obvious that recombination between the two rII mutants has occurred with the production of wild types. The number of plaques on strain B gives information on the total number of infective centers, permitting calculation of the recombination frequency.

The length of the map unit corresponding to a mutational alteration can be determined if there are two closely linked genes on either side (Fig. 16). The length corresponding to mutation 2 can be determined by determining the map distances 1 to 2, 1 to 3 and 2 to 3 if the order of the genes is known to be 123. The maximum length (on the genetic map, that is, in recombination units) of 2 would be given by the difference of the genetic distance 1 to 3 from the sum of the distances 1 to 2 and 2 to 3. This method depends on the fact that recombination percentages are additive (approximately) throughout the genetic map.

Benzer's method for translating the recombination frequencies

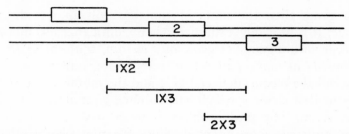

Figure 16. Method for determining the "length" of a mutation. The discrepancy between the long distance and the sum of the two short distances measures the length of the central mutation. All distances are measured as recombination fractions. (Benzer, in McElroy and Glass, Chemical Basis of Heredity, Johns Hopkins Press, 1957.)

into nucleotide pairs is extremely approximate but does lead to an important conclusion. The primary assumption is important enough to be repeated: since in all experiments the genetic material seems to be arranged in one dimension, that is, in linear array, it is assumed that some linear property of the DNA molecule is the important genetic fact. The most obvious linear property is the order of the bases, that is, their sequence and this order is therefore assumed to carry the genetic information. A corollary of this idea is that it will be impossible to separate pure DNA, chemically, in the same sense that one can separate pure benzoic acid or even pure insulin. Since DNA is isolated *en masse* from organisms, it represents a collection of genes. Isolation of a pure DNA in the sense of a set of molecules each with a different and unique base order would require a chemical separation of the individual genes. From the practical point of view this experimental operation seems impossible to achieve with the techniques now available.

The total DNA of bacteriophage T4 contains about 4×10^5 nucleotides. It is assumed that this DNA is in the form of one large piece containing 40 per cent of the DNA and many smaller pieces; the 40 per cent piece seems to be passed to phage progeny and is therefore identified as the genetic material for the purpose of this calculation (Levinthal 1956, Stent, Sato and Jerne 1959). Therefore there are 1.6×10^5 nucleotides in the phage genetic material. It is assumed that there is one copy of each gene and that the genetic material occurs in a Watson-Crick double helix giving 8×10^4 nucleotide pairs in the genetic material. The total length of the T4 genetic map is estimated by Benzer (1957) as 800 recombination units. This total is estimated by extrapolating the measured recombination frequencies for a small region to the whole organism. Most often the total is estimated by adding together all the measured recombination frequencies. Obviously as the recombination values become large it is impossible to distinguish linked genes from unlinked genes recombining by independent assortment. Long genetic maps are therefore constructed by adding together the smaller recombination frequencies. Finally, it is assumed that the probability of recombination per unit length of the genetic map and per nucleotide unit is uniform. This last assumption may or may not be justified. In Drosophila, where it has been possible to compare cytological distance on the chromosome with map distance obtained from recombination studies, it can be seen that there is a "bunching up" of recombination at certain places along the chromosome. The gene order is always that given by the genetic maps but the distances between genes are not as uniform as predicted from the recombination frequencies. The Drosophila chromosome is a very complex morphological and chemical structure compared to the phage linkage groups and the assumption made by Benzer may be reasonable for phages.

In a system of 8×10^4 nucleotide pairs and with 800 map units 0.01 per cent recombination would correspond to the separation of single nucleotide pairs. The smallest percentage of recombination obtained by Benzer was 0.02 per cent which means that the *recon*, the "smallest element in the one dimensional array interchangeable but not divisible by genetic recombination," is equal to two nucleotide pairs (or 8 nucleotide pairs if a map distance of 200 is taken). Benzer's estimate of the size of the *muton* is 5 nucleotide pairs while the cistron, or the functional gene, is a very complex structure of hundreds or thousands of nucleotide pairs.

Pontecorvo (1956, 1958) has used a similar method to calculate the size of the different genetic elements in Aspergillus and in Drosophila. One obtains the lowest fraction of the total map observed to recombine and multiplies this fraction by the total number of nucleotide pairs in the DNA to obtain the number of nucleotide pairs in the *recon* (Table 6). For Aspergillus the value comes out as three nucleotide pairs while for Drosophila (assuming each gene occurs only once in a Watson-Crick double helix, an assumption which seems required by the facts of genetics even though it ignores the multistranded structure of the chromosomes) there are 40 nucleotide pairs in the *recon*. Since the smallest re-

TABLE 6.   *Smallest Recombination Fractions Measured in Four Organisms Expressed as Fractions of the Total DNA**

	TOTAL LINKAGE MAP UNITS	TOTAL DNA IN NUCLEO- TIDE PAIRS	NUCLEOTIDE PAIRS PER MAP UNIT	MINIMUM RECOM- BINATION FRACTION MEASURED (a)	(a) AS FRACTIONS OF TOTAL MAP	(a) AS FRACTION OF TOTAL DNA IN NUCLEOTIDE PAIRS
Phage T4	800	2×10^5	2.5×10^2	1×10^{-4}	1×10^{-5}	2
Escherichia coli	2000	1×10^7	5×10^3	2×10^{-5}	1×10^{-6}	10
Aspergillus	660	4×10^7	7×10^4	1×10^{-6}	1.5×10^{-7}	3
Drosophila	280	8×10^7	3×10^5	8×10^{-6}	2×10^{-6}	40

* From Pontecorvo, Trends in Genetic Analysis, Columbia University Press, 1958.

combination fraction depends in part on the number of progeny scored except in phages, where the lowest fraction obtained is far higher than the fraction which could, theoretically, be detected, there is every reason to believe that these figures are maximum values. Pontecorvo (1956) has stated that he has never obtained a mutation in Aspergillus which failed to recombine with a "recurrence" and the best extrapolation of the data may be that recombination can occur between any two nucleotide pairs. If the DNA is a continuous sequence of genetically meaningful nucleotide pairs this means that recombination cannot distinguish between different genetic elements.

Pontecorvo also calculates the possible number of mutable sites within each cistron on the assumption that the minimum recombination values obtained with Drosophila and Aspergillus do have some meaning. One divides the recombination value between the two sites in the same cistron furthest apart by the recombination value of the two sites closest together. The value obtained indicates the possible number of sites within each cistron. For Aspergillus Pontecorvo obtained values of over 1000 sites possible in the two cistrons for which data were given (Table 7). The total size of the cistron can therefore be estimated to be from 1000 to 8000 nucleotide pairs. As an exercise I have calculated the values for Neurospora and it turns out that if there are 1000 nucleotide pairs per cistron then Neurospora has about 6000 genes in each haploid nucleus. It is only fair to point out that these calculations are based on a series of tenuous assumptions. However they do indicate the great resolving power of the recombination process.

The experiments make it possible to suggest a definition of the gene. The gene is a unit of function as determined by the *cis-trans* test or by suitable biochemical tests. There are independently mutating sites within the gene and gene parts can be separated by the process or processes of recombination. Recombination can occur between genes or within genes and recombination can give a unit made up partly of one allele and partly of another. This implies that recombination should at times give progeny with unexpected properties, different from either parent, and this has been observed (Bradley 1958).

I have also indicated a confusing issue in the definition of the gene. From the geneticists' point of view the *cis-trans* test has the greatest specificity and should be the only functional test. On the other hand, the evidence linking genes with the determination of particular polypeptide amino acid sequences is reasonably good and to a biochemist this should be the conclusive test of whether two genes control the same function: that is, two genes affecting the same polypeptide are by definition part of the same

TABLE 7. *Examples from Three Organisms of the Rates of Recombination between Mutational Sites of One Gene (Cistron)* *

ORGANISM AND GENE	MUTATIONAL SITES SO FAR IDENTIFIED NO.	SUM OF RECOMBINATION FRACTIONS BETWEEN THE TWO OUTERMOST SITES (a)	RECOMBINATION FRACTION BETWEEN THE TWO CLOSEST (b)	INFERRED MINIMAL NUMBER OF SITES PER CISTRON RATIOS a/b	a/b
Drosophila					
bx	5	3×10^{-4}	3×10^{-5}	10	37
1z	3	1.4×10^{-3}	6×10^{-4}	2.5	187
w	4	5.6×10^{-4}	8×10^{-6}†	70	70
Aspergillus					
bi	3	1×10^{-3}	4×10^{-4}	2.5	1000
ad8	6	1.8×10^{-3}	15×10^{-6}	360	1800
paba	2		1×10^{-6}†		
pro3	2		1×10^{-6}†		
Phage T4					
r(II)A	39	4.3×10^{-2}	1.3×10^{-4}†	330	330
r(II)B	18	3.5×10^{-2}	1×10^{-3}	35	269
h	6	2.0×10^{-2}	2×10^{-4}	100	153

* From Pontecorvo, Trends in Genetic Analysis, Columbia University Press, 1958.
† Indicates the smallest recombination fraction so far measured in each organism.
The ratio a/b estimates the possible number of intervals or sites in the different genes.

cistron. The discovery of complementation in Neurospora makes it impossible to accept both of these definitions. Woodward *et al.* (1958) talk, very properly, about different *cistrons* affecting the same protein—which is the meaning of the production of adenyl-succinase by heterocaryons. But this does not seem proper *if* adenylsuccinase (and the other enzymes involved in cases of complementation) are single polypeptide chains. If these enzymes turn out to be similar in structure to the tryptophan synthetase of *E. coli* described by Crawford and Yanofsky (1958) then both ideas may be preserved. Tryptophan synthetase in *E. coli* is a conglomerate of two protein components which can be separated but have enzyme activity only when combined.

The best theoretical definition of the gene seems to me to be "that section of the DNA involved in the determination of the amino acid sequence of a single peptide." Unfortunately biochemical knowledge is not advanced enough operationally to rely on the definition. Confusions such as those introduced by the complementation phenomenon are bound to arise in the application of the *cis-trans* test but these confusions may only indicate areas in which more biochemical work is needed.

IV. *The Mechanism of Recombination*

We have used the phenomenon of recombination to define and discuss the nature of the gene without inquiring too much about the nature of the process itself. It is necessary to inquire whether the recombination process is the same in all organisms and to inquire whether there is any relationship between gene multiplication and recombination.

In organisms with definite chromosomes it seems most likely that recombination occurs at the four strand stage (as discussed earlier) but that only two strands recombine at any one time. All four strands *can* participate in the recombination process (that is, if two crossovers occur in the same chromosome pair all four of the strands may be involved) which shows that there is no distinction between parental and daughter strands as far as recombination ability is concerned. (According to the Watson-Crick idea of DNA structure each one of the four chromatids contains one parental and one new DNA strand in its double helix, making the distinction between parental and daughter strands impossible, but this may be too simple an idea of chromosome structure.) It is

78

required that the complementary or reciprocal recombinants be produced by a single event in order to account for the genetic results. It is assumed as a result of the genetic experiments that the recombination points are exactly matched in the two interacting strands. It is further assumed by most geneticists that the process of recombination is closely related to the process of meiosis since during the pairing of chromosomes in meiosis (synapsis) there is an exact, point to point, pairing of analogous points on homologous chromosomes. This pairing is so specific that it causes the formation of visible rings and other abnormalities if one chromosome pairs with a homologue in which the sequence of genes has been inverted (inversions) (*cf.* Srb and Owen 1951).

This specific pairing has caused many—probably most—geneticists to accept the chiasmatype theory of crossing over which supposes that recombination occurs after the pairing of synapsis and is related to the formation of *chiasmata* (cytologically visible crossing of chromosome strands) during meiosis. The idea supposes that two chromatids split in two parts in exactly analogous positions and then rejoin with an exchange of partners. Chemically this is both an amazing and fascinating idea since it supposes a physical separation of a chromosome made of protein(s) and nucleic acid(s) followed by restoration without any further effects. (There is evidence that chromosome breaks induced by radiation require metabolic processes for their restoration, Wolff and Luippold 1955.) Not only that, two chromosomes must simultaneously break in the same place. There have been some recent suppositions, partly supported by experiments with chelating agents (Steffensen 1957), that the chromosomes are really held together by divalent ions and that recombination occurs between pieces held together by such divalent ions. It seems to me that this is not a sufficient explanation because of the ability of even the smallest amounts of genetic material to recombine. There is another chemical consequence of the idea that recombination occurs at the time of meiosis, namely that recombination is not related to gene duplication since DNA reproduction occurs before the time of chromosome condensation and synapsis (Taylor 1957).

In microorganisms,. particularly in bacteriophage, the situation is quite different since complementary recombinants are *not* produced by a single event. The evidence for this idea has been summarized by Hershey (1957) and the important facts are (a) there is no correlated production of complementary types by a single bacterium (when populations of infected bacteria are studied it is found that both types of recombinants are produced on the average, but this complementarity does not exist when the individual bacteria are studied), (b) heterozygotes are formed which produce only single recombinants. Slight doses of UV irradiation markedly increase the recombination rate (Jacob and Wollman 1955). If a single mutant characteristic, or "marker," is studied it is found that large numbers of lesions induced by radiation do not affect the replication of the marker or its recombination with undamaged bacteriophage. In the molecular autoradiographic method of Levinthal (1956) it was shown that the large piece of DNA retains its integrity throughout many matings even though extensive recombination does occur. These facts are not easily explained on the basis of the standard method of recombination in higher organisms which does appear to be a reciprocal exchange. One would expect single bacteria to give both types of recombinants (Visconti and Delbruck (1953) were able to account for the facts on the basis of the ideas of reciprocal recombination and of population genetics) and one would not expect the large DNA piece to retain its integrity through many rounds of mating.

The new hypothesis is generally called the "copy-choice" mechanism (Lederberg 1955). It supposes that a new strand of DNA is formed using one of the parental strands as a model. Occasionally, as when the strand meets a site damaged by UV irradiation, the new strand will "switch over" and copy from the other parental strand. The genetic result of the "copy-choice" phenomenon is recombination related to gene duplication. The explanation does fit the facts and is commonly accepted as a working hypothesis. But it does not give a picture of the molecular events. The detailed mechanisms of the splitting of the double helices, their unwinding and the copying first from one model and then from another are as completely obscure as is the mechanism by which chromosomes are supposed to break apart and recombine in reciprocal recombination.

This copy-choice mechanism is not limited to the bacteriophage. In Neurospora and in yeast there have been reported a number of cases in which crosses of two alleles lead to the production of the wild type but without producing the double mutant recombinant. Alleles now imply two or more forms of a gene with differences in the same cistron whether at the same or different sites. Although there has been some confusion about terminology, this phenomenon is now called "gene conversion." In this case non-reciprocal recombination occurs in organisms which have mechanisms for reciprocal recombination. An instructive experiment on these events has been performed by Roman and Jacob (1958). In yeast, UV irradiation increases the rate of recombination between alleles (non-reciprocal recombination) but it does not affect the recombination of genes far away from one another (Table 8). We would expect on the basis of the "orthodox" mechanism that

TABLE 8.   *The Effect of Ultraviolet Light on Recombination in Yeast**

A. THE EFFECT OF UV LIGHT ON THE FREQUENCY OF ALLELIC RECOMBINATION

GENOTYPE	PER CENT SURVIVAL	REVERSIONS/ 10^6 SURVIVORS
H i_a t/h i_b T	100	172
	82	870
	61	2314
h i_a T/H i_b t	100	304
	90	936
	27	4135
H i_a t/h i_a T	100	0.3
	78	102
	46	320
H i_b t/h i_b T	100	0.4
	87	40
	70	136

B. EVIDENCE FOR RECOMBINATION BETWEEN OUTSIDE MARKERS AMONG REVERTANTS AND NON-REVERTANTS OF H i_a t/h i_b T

UV	NUMBER TESTED	REVERTANTS WITH REQUIREMENTS FOR			
		h	t	ht	%
	1-Among *i* revertants				
0	360	38	5	5	1
0	360	38	5	5	13.3
45"	288	4	8	0	4.2
90"	327	1	9	1	3.4
	2-Among non-revertants				
0	144	0	0	0	
45"	144	0	1	0	
90"	288	3	4	0	2.4

* Data from Roman and Jacob, 1958.

Reversion indicates the change from isoleucine requirement (*i*) to non-requirement. Histidine requirement is represented by h, tryptophan requirement by t, isoleucine requirement by the two alleles i_a and i_b. H and T represent the dominant non-requiring alleles.

separation of the two parts of a gene preparatory to a recombination would also result in the separation of two different mutant genes located on opposite sides of the mutant gene being studied. But this is exactly what does not happen after UV irradiation. Non-reciprocal recombination, that is, gene conversion, is normally associated with an abnormally high frequency of crossovers between outside markers (the mutant genes on opposite sides of the one studied) indicating that a close geometric association of the chromosomes may be required. Irradiation, however, does not increase the frequency with which the outside markers recombine although it does increase the frequency of intra-allelic recombination. Roman's experiment indicates that there may be two distinct mechanisms of recombination in some organisms, one standard, the other "copy-choice."

There are studies with Drosophila which can best be explained by supposing that recombination is related to chromosome duplication (Schwartz 1954). If this were generally true, it would be necessary to separate the processes of chromosome duplication and of gene or DNA duplication. Perhaps this is what does happen. Roman's work does suggest two separate mechanisms for recombination. Pontecorvo (1958) points out that there is really no evidence that recombination occurs at meiosis and it may be that there is only one mechanism of recombination at the time of gene duplication and that the necessity of postulating two mechanisms is caused by some "genetic block" in our thinking rather than because of the physical facts themselves.

Notwithstanding doubts about the mechanism, the fact of recombination is of primary importance for genetics. But the implications of recombination include more than a mechanism for the exchange of genetic material. One of the easiest suppositions about the origin of genetic change or mutation is that mutation represents a change in the order of the bases of DNA. In "copy-choice" mechanisms and also in standard recombination mechanisms the progeny strand has a DNA base order which is different from either of the parents. When recombination occurs within a gene this is particularly significant. The mistake in copying base orders in mutation may certainly be analogous to the switch in copying base orders in the copy-choice mechanisms and the difference between mutation and recombination is therefore one of the agent inducing the mutation. We might even expect recombination to have a mutagenic effect at times and there are scattered investigations which do show just such an effect. Bradley (1958) has shown that an unexpectedly high frequency of segregants from heterocaryons of Streptomyces have growth requirements different from those of either of the original strains; Mangelsdorf (1958) has presented some evidence for the mutagenic effect of hybridizing maize with teosinte, and Brink (1958) has described a phenomenon he calls "paramutation" in which there is a directed mutation which invariably occurs in certain maize heterozygotes. Some of these cases may be explained by the segregation of particular modifier genes as in the case described by Haskins and Mitchell (1952) in which modifiers apparently changed the position of the genetic block in Neurospora. It is also quite possible that the process of recombination results in mutation or that the process of gene conversion (occurring by copy-choice) results in a different base order which is actually a mutation. If so, we may expect to find other cases in which mutation is produced as a result of recombination.

Chapter Four

Mutation as a Chemical Process

"*Any inherited* change not due to segregation or the normal recombination of unchanged genetic material" (Wagner and Mitchell 1955) is defined as a mutation. Mutation is therefore fundamental to the study of genetics since it leads to the diversity which makes genetics meaningful—study in genetics is always the study of differences between organisms—and because the characteristics of the mutation process should give as important clues to the nature of the genetic material as does the study of recombination.

The study of mutation was begun early in the history of genetics, long before there were adequate ideas about the molecular nature of the genetic material or of the nature of gene reproduction. As a consequence there are a plethora of observations and a minimum of acceptable generalizations. The situation is in sharp contrast to that described in the first three chapters and it is necessary to treat the material in a slightly different manner. It may be that we are at the start of a period in which the phenomena of mutation can be treated in a rational way. On the other hand it may be that the approach adopted here will turn out to be incorrect. It seems more reasonable to adopt a hypothesis and determine its consequences than to present a series of empirical observations. The reader is warned that these interpretations are only tentative.

I. *Detection of Gene Mutations*

It has been fairly well established that the genetic material is DNA, that this is present in a Watson-Crick double helix and that the genetic material is arranged in linear array down to the smallest subdivision (Benzer 1959). Since the genetic alphabet must be the sequence of nucleotides, any change in the sequence should cause a change in the genetic message. Changes which can be detected are mutations and we will attempt to define a *gene mutation* as a detectable change in the phenotype caused by a change in nucleotide base sequence within the DNA. Our problem is to find some method for operationally detecting gene mutations and separating them from other genetic changes.

It has become difficult to distinguish between mutation and recombination (Chapter 3). The change from streptomycin sensitivity to resistance is not considered a bacterial mutation if the change results from the introduction of the resistance factor by a bacterial mating process, by transduction or by a DNA transforming factor. The change is mutation if it is a change in base order induced by a mutagenic agent or occurring spontaneously. The intragenic recombination of two allelic mutants to give the wild type by a "copy-choice" or gene conversion mechanism really differs only in degree from true mutation. Since the processes may lead to an *intra*genic order of nucleotide bases that was not present in either parent they might almost as well be classified mutations as recombinations.

Many types of genetic change can cause changes in the phenotype. In higher organisms it is often possible to distinguish *chromosome mutations* (caused by inversion in the gene order of the chromosome or by translocation of a particular gene to another chromosome) from gene mutations. It is also possible, in some cases, to separate a class of deletions caused by a loss of chromosomal material from the class of gene mutations. Obviously, if part of the genetic material has been removed, the genes included within the deleted segment do not operate. As the deletions pass below the visible region it becomes operationally impossible to separate a minute deletion from a gene mutation and as a result there have been many discussions about the relative proportion of gene mutation and minute deletions produced by different mutagenic treatments (Stadler 1954). A reasonable hypothesis is that any mutant that can return to its original condition by a second mutation at the same genetic site (*reversion* or *back mutation*) is a gene mutation rather than a deletion since it is difficult to account for the spontaneous appearance of genetic material but not too difficult to envisage the reversal of a process leading to changed genetic material. With most microorganisms it is difficult, if not impossible, to distinguish between gene and chromosomal mutation and in almost all investigations there is no attempt to make the distinction.

Studies of mutation require a method for the quantitative estimation of the number of mutations produced. Since mutation is at best a rare event any method for the quantitative estimation of mutation rate must be able to detect a small number of events occurring in a large population. *Selection methods* are therefore almost always part of any procedure for the detection of mutations.

Perhaps the simplest measure of mutation (considering mainly the microorganisms) is the determination of resistance to some drug, virus or other toxic agent. A suspension of microorganisms is treated and then plated on a medium containing the drug or virus. Only mutant cells which are resistant can grow on a medium which contains the virus or drug and so the classification and selection procedures are identical. Much of the early development of microbial genetics was concerned with the question of whether the resistant cells were produced in response to the virus or drug or were merely selected by them. A recondite analysis by Luria and Delbruck (1943) showed that the bacteriophages used for the measurement of phage-resistant mutants were merely selective and there are now two simple techniques available, one developed by Newcombe (1949) and the other based on the replica plating technique of the Lederbergs (1952) (described in the first chapter), which demonstrate this fact more easily. In Newcombe's technique cells are spread on plates and are allowed to incubate long enough for microcolonies to develop. The cells are then respread, sprayed with virus and incubated until visible colonies appear. It is found that many more colonies appear after respreading than appear without this treatment. If the selection technique *induced* the mutations we would expect that all cells would be equally likely to be affected and respreading would have no effect. If the technique *selects* random spontaneous mutants then respreading should make a big difference because of the increase in the number of mutants caused by reproduction of those mutants present and produced in the preliminary incubation period. The offspring of a single resistant mutant cell would all be concentrated in a single colony before respreading but would form many resistant colonies after respreading.

The replica plating technique can be used to test offspring of single colonies for resistance without exposing the original colony to the selective agent. Once the resistant colony has been identified it can be shown that 100 per cent of the cells obtained from this colony are resistant in contrast to the very small percentage usually obtained from the original population.

It is possible to plate on selective medium when a measure of the spontaneous mutation frequency is desired. ("Spontaneous" mutations are those which appear without any treatment with a mutagenic agent.) If the mutagenic effect of a particular agent is being studied it is often necessary to incubate in a complete medium following treatment or even to permit several cell divisions to take place before the maximum number of mutations is obtained. The reason for this requirement is not completely known; probably there are several reasons and the phenomenon will be discussed later.

Mutation frequency generally indicates the number of mutants present per survivor or per cell treated. Since most mutagenic agents also have a lethal effect, the number of mutants per survivor is often used as a measure but it is an assumption that this represents a true value for the total population. In all the methods used with microorganisms one usually plates a large number of organisms on a petri plate; it is assumed that the very small proportion of mutant organisms will form colonies without interference from the larger number of non-mutant organisms. Obviously this too is an assumption, one not always justified by the facts and it is necessary to carry out determinations of the interference effect of the non-mutant population (Grigg 1952, Stevens and Mylroie 1953) before utilizing any particular procedure.

A useful method for the estimation of mutant number is the technique of studying the back mutation or reversion of nutritionally deficient mutant strains (Jensen *et al.* 1951). The mutant strains will not grow on a minimal medium, the wild type strains will grow and the change from requirement to non-requirement or from *auxotrophy* to *prototrophy* can therefore be used as a measure of mutation. There are a number of gene changes other than back mutation that might result in a change from auxotrophy to prototrophy. The alternatives have been discussed at length by M.

Green (1957) and include recombination events, gene "conversion" effects, position effects and changes at non-allelic loci such as suppressor and modifier mutations. The distinction between suppressor and reverse mutation can be made with any organisms in which recombination can be observed, but the method is particularly simple (in theory) with Neurospora. Suppose in Neurospora that there is a mutant gene *m* and that some other gene has mutated from its + allele to give a suppressor, *s*, resulting in a prototrophic organism. The genetic composition of the prototroph is therefore *ms*. If we cross this strain to a true wild type we will have the cross *ms* × ++. Remembering that the segregation of genes is ordered in the ascus and that each gene may segregate in either the first or second division (Chapter 3) we may have any of the following:

(a) *ms*	(b) *m*+	(c) *ms*
ms	*m*+	*m*+
++	+*s*	+*s*
++	+*s*	++

The + *s* combination is usually prototrophic. Combination (a) gives all prototrophic spores, (b) gives 50 per cent mutant and 50 per cent prototrophic spores. Both these combinations might be expected in back mutation, if there were some mutant nuclei carried along in heterocaryotic condition. Combination (c) gives a ratio of three prototrophs to one mutant and when this combination is obtained it is evidence that the strain carries a suppressor mutation and is not a true back mutant.

Even though a nutritional mutant develops the ability to grow without the addition of a growth supplement as a result of a change at the original mutant locus, this does not mean that the mutant allele has mutated back to the *original* condition. There is a fairly extensive literature on iso-alleles—genes differing only slightly in their effects—and Giles (1958) has some fairly definite evidence that reversions in Neurospora (not caused by suppressor mutation) need not be changes to the *original* genetic condition (see below). The methods used for the selection of mutants and the types of mutation selected for study may determine the results of an experiment. A particular selection method may select only mutants of a particular type with a resultant bias in our attitude about the process studied.

II. *Production of Mutations by Changes in Base Order*

Metabolic antagonists can be divided into two major classes: those that are incorporated into biologically important molecules to yield abnormal substances and those that act immediately as enzyme inhibitors. The amino acid analogue ethionine (the analogue of methionine) and the analogue fluorophenylalanine are both inhibitors but they act by being incorporated into protein molecules (Gross and Tarver 1955, Munier and Cohen 1956). The protein molecule containing these abnormal constituents may or may not be functional. The amino acid tryptazan is incorporated into protein in place of tryptophan (Brawerman and Ycas 1957) but the analogue methyltryptophan is not incorporated and in fact inhibits the first enzymatic step involved in the incorporation of tryptophan into protein (Sharon and Lipman 1957).

The thymine analogue, 5-bromouracil, can be incorporated into bacteriophage and into bacteria in place of thymine. As many as 9 per cent of the phage particles yield viable progeny even when all of the thymine is substituted by bromouracil (Litman and Pardee 1956). When the cells are again incubated in a medium with no analogue the bromouracil in the DNA is replaced by the normal thymine on continued reproduction. Bromouracil also greatly increases the frequency with which bacteriophage mutants are obtained. In a typical experiment (Freese 1959a) infected bacteria are incubated and allowed to lyse in a medium containing bromouracil and sulfanilamide or aminopterin. Sulfanilamide and aminopterin act to prevent the biosynthesis of thymine and therefore promote the incorporation of the analogue. A more direct method is to use a thymine-requiring mutant for the work. In the experiments to be discussed, mutants at the rII locus (Chapter 3) were induced by bromouracil treatment and were analyzed genetically. Other analogues can also be incorporated and be mutagenic. Isoadenine, 2-aminopurine, is incorporated into the DNA and is mutagenic as is 2,6-diaminopurine (Fig. 17). (Other substances which are not incorporated into phage are mutagenic. UV light, nitrogen mustard, streptomycin and proflavine—3,6-diaminoacridine—are mutagenic when applied to the phage-bacterium complex.)

The genetic structure of the rII locus of the bacteriophage T4 has been mapped almost to the nucleotide level (Benzer 1957) and it is possible to find out whether there are any local differences

in the response of the genetic material to particular types of mutagens. Such differences do exist. There are regions within a single
cistron that are particularly likely to mutate in response to a
particular mutagen. Mutations induced by bromouracil tend to
occur at locations different from those induced by proflavine and
these in turn occur at locations different from the spontaneous
mutations and those induced by aminopurine (Brenner *et al.* 1958,
Freese 1959a). The specificity of response of the genetic material to
different mutagens indicates that particular types of molecular
transition are involved.

Freese supposes that it is possible to predict which analogues
are likely to be mutagenic because of the existence of certain requirements imposed by the Watson-Crick structure and by the
facts of enzymology. The mutagenic base must be able to form
two hydrogen bonds with both purine or both pyrimidine bases
and it must also be convertible into the deoxynucleotide triphosphate (the normal DNA precursor) by enzyme systems present in
the cell.

Is it possible to make any definite statement about the type of
molecular change involved in mutation? Many phage mutants are

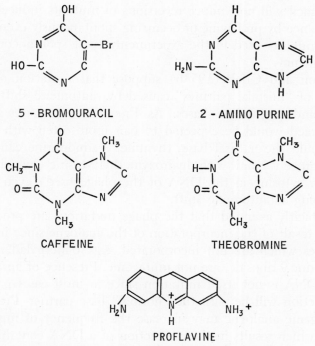

Figure 17. Some mutagenic base analogues.

TABLE 9. *Induction of Reversions in Bacteriophage Mutants by Bromouracil**

REVERTING MUTANTS WHICH WERE ORIGINALLY OBTAINED BY TREATMENT WITH	TOTAL NUMBER	INDUCIBLE		NONINDUCIBLE	
		NUMBER	%	NUMBER	%
BD† + 4 × thymidine	100	80	80	20	20
5-Bromouracil	64	61	95	3	5
2-Aminopurine	98	96	98	2	2
Spontaneous mutants	110	15	14	95	86
Proflavine	55	1	2	54	98

* From Freese, Proc. Nat. Acad. Sci. U.S., vol. 45, 1959.
† BD = 5-bromodeoxyuridine

able to revert to the wild type condition regardless of the mutagenic treatment employed in their production. Even "spontaneous" mutants are able to revert. A series of mutants was induced by bromouracil, aminopurine, proflavine and a series of spontaneous mutants was also selected. Only mutations that would spontaneously revert were tested. Freese (1959b) showed that bromouracil would induce reversions only among those strains induced in the first instance by bromouracil or aminopurine (Table 9). Bromouracil will not *induce* reversions of mutants induced in the first instance by proflavine or occurring spontaneously even though all the mutants used in the experiment revert spontaneously at a low frequency.

Watson and Crick (1953b) suppose that mutation occurs as a result of "mistake pairings" caused by tautomeric shifts in the purine and pyrimidine bases. As Freese demonstrates (1959a) bromouracil would be expected to pair more often with guanine than would the natural base, thymine. Aminopurine can pair by one hydrogen bond with hydroxymethylcytosine (which substitutes for cytosine in the DNA of the phage used) even without undergoing a tautomeric shift.

It is tacitly assumed that the phage mutations are produced as a direct result of the incorporation of the analogue since inhibitory analogues which are not incorporated, *e.g.*, 6-methyladenine, purine, purine-9-riboside, are not mutagenic. Presence of an analogue in the DNA is not itself mutation since in most cases pairing on reproduction will be with the "normal" base partner. Presence of a mutagenic analogue may increase the frequency of mistakes in pairing which results in the production of a DNA containing only the natural bases but with a different base order. It is the change of normal base order which is significant because only this can be reproduced in a normal environment. Mutation has occurred *only* when a change has been introduced into the DNA which can be propagated indefinitely.

Two types of base substitution are distinguished by Freese. In "mistakes in incorporation" a guanine residue (in the DNA chain) pairs with bromouracil during DNA duplication. This error leads to the substitution of an adenine-thymine pair for the original guanine-hydroxymethylcytosine. "Mistakes in replication" occur after bromouracil has been incorporated in place of thymine in the DNA chain. Bromouracil may then pair with guanine by mistake during duplication leading in the end to a substitution of a guanine-hydroxymethylcytosine pair for the original adenine-thymine.

The specificity of bromouracil in the induction of reversions of mutations originally induced by base analogues is accounted for by supposing that agents such as proflavine, heat or thymine-starvation (Kanazir 1958) result in a structural change which is different in kind from the change induced by the incorporated analogues. Freese defines changes of this second sort as "transversions." In transversions nucleotide pairs are changed so that a purine is replaced by a pyrimidine or *vice versa*. The assumed substitutions in transversions do not fit the Watson-Crick structure but it is assumed that the agents inducing this type of change result in a deformation of the structure sufficient to permit the change. It is also supposed that the whole Watson-Crick structure is large enough to carry a minute lesion along for one division. This type of purine for pyrimidine substitution cannot be reversed by analogues which bring about purine for purine or pyrimidine for pyrimidine substitutions. If the hypothesis is correct, then the class of mutation or mutagen can be determined by the type of mutagen necessary to induce reversion.

If it is assumed that mutagenesis by the analogues is a result of a change in a single nucleotide pair, reversions of almost all induced mutations should occur and the mutations should be sharply localized in the genome—as is the case (Freese 1959a, b). The data also seem to require the assumption that the muton and the recon (Chapter 3) are identical units, both equal, in the last analysis, to the most elementary unit of DNA structure, the nucleotide pair.

The technique of studying mutation by the use of base analogues is so far restricted to the bacteriophage. It has been reported that bromouracil is either not mutagenic for bacteria (Novick 1956) or that it produces many mutants of the slow growing type (Zamenhof *et al.* 1957). No analysis comparable to that made with bacteriophage has been attempted with other organisms probably because there are no cases in which the genetic map is as well defined.

While it is reasonable to suppose that a change in a single base pair can lead to a detectable mutation in bacteriophage it is unlikely that all mutations in all organisms represent such a simple change. Freese supposes that the deformation of the DNA structure involved in the transversion mechanism may lead to alterations in the molecule more drastic than the substitution of a single nucleotide pair. A number of cases in which "partial reversions" have been obtained from enzymatically deficient mutants also support this idea (Giles *et al.* 1957, Fincham 1957), especially since there is some evidence that the enzyme formed by the revertants is not identical with the enzyme produced by the wild type (Stadler and Yanofsky 1959). If it is assumed that a change in a single base pair leads to an enzyme with a changed amino acid sequence then there should be at most four possible enzyme molecules produced as a result of changes in the base pairs at any one nucleotide pair site within the DNA. These would be the wild type enzyme (original base pair), the mutant (non-functional) enzyme and two intermediates which might be partially functional. If more than two intermediates, different from both mutant and original wild type, are obtained from the reversion of any particular strain, then it is necessary that more than one base pair has been affected by the mutation. It is likely that this situation occurs often.

III. Mutagens Which Act on DNA

Certain other defined structural changes in DNA lead to mutation. It is known that the decay of P-32 in DNA is lethal to bacteria and that this lethality is independent of the beta radiation accompanying the decay, that is that the effect is caused by transmutation. Recently Kaudewitz *et al.* (1958) have presented some convincing evidence that the decay of incorporated P-32 is mutagenic. A variety of nutritional requirements were induced by P-32 decay in *E. coli*. The mutant colonies produced often had wild type sectors; in a large proportion of the cases the wild type sector represented half the colony. The simplest interpretation is that transmutation results in the rupture of the P-O bonds holding one of the DNA polynucleotide chains together but has no effect on the second chain. At cell division one normal and one abnormal DNA are formed leading to a sectored colony. It is not clear just how the P-O bond cleavage leads to a substitution of bases. Since back mutation of P-32 induced mutants or the induction of reversion by P-32 transmutation has not yet been reported it is not known whether these are gene mutations or inactivations. One would suspect that P-32 acted to produce "transversions" but at any rate the transmutation method permits the study of the mutagenic effect of a distinct structural change in DNA.

Nitrous acid will produce mutations in tobacco mosaic virus when isolated virus RNA is treated with this reagent (Gierer and Mundry 1958, Mundry 1959). Nitrous acid is a well known reagent of organic chemistry which substitutes hydroxyl groups for amino groups. Reaction of nitrous acid with the nucleic acid bases which contain amino groups, adenine, guanine and cytosine, converts these to the corresponding hydroxyl compounds, hypoxanthine, xanthine and uracil. It is implied by these experiments that reaction of nitrous acid with nucleic acid produces base analogues *in situ* which result in mutation on duplication of the genetic material. In some cases the protein of the mutant TMV virus produced by treatment of isolated virus RNA with nitrous acid followed by reconstitution has an altered amino acid composition (Tsugita and Fraenkel-Conrat 1960).

Treatment with nitrous acid results in the production of auxotrophic mutants of the bacterium *Escherichia coli* (Kaudewitz 1959a, b). In contrast to the results obtained by P-32 transmutation, none of the mutant colonies obtained was sectored, that is, had wild type cells present. This result and an analysis of the kinetics of mutant production led Kaudewitz to suggest that nitrous acid must affect both strands of the bacterial DNA in order to produce mutation.

It is both curious and amusing that the mutagenic effects of nitrous acid were reported by Thom and Steinberg (1939, Steinberg and Thom 1940) many years ago but that the discovery was ignored by most geneticists. Thom analyzed his results in a manner similar to the analysis of Gierer and of Kaudewitz except that he considered the genetic material to be protein (as was fashionable at that time) and considered the reaction to be deamination of the amino acids. Before 1940 geneticists just did not believe that chemical substances induced mutation and, since Thom worked with poorly defined mutants of a fungus, Aspergillus, his results were, for the most part, discounted.

During the war it was recognized by the pharmacologist Robson that the war gases of the "mustard gas" type were *radiomimetic*, that is, that their effects mimicked those of radiation. Auerbach and Robson (1946) were then able to show that both nitrogen and sulfur mustards were mutagenic and duplicated the effect of radiation in this respect also. This information was released after the war and within a few years many compounds were shown to be mutagenic. It is somewhat surprising to realize that before 1940 there was no accepted demonstration that any chemical substance was mutagenic whereas recently it has almost seemed that any substance can be shown to produce mutations—including such common chemicals as $MnCl_2$ (Demerec and Hanson 1951), $NaNO_2$ and caffeine (Novick and Szilard 1951). I suspect that there are at least two reasons for this: first, the acceptance of the microorganisms as tools for genetic research and, secondly, the change in attitude which followed the unequivocable demonstration by Auerbach and Robson that chemical substances could be mutagenic. Changes had been produced in microorganisms but before about 1947 there were many who doubted that the genetic system in bacteria and asexual molds could be compared to that of higher organisms.

One of the major classes of chemical mutagens is the alkylating agents: organic reagents which will transfer alkyl groups to other compounds (Table 10). Compounds of this type are often carcinogenic and their derivatives are used in cancer therapy. No one knows whether there is a relationship between their carcinogenic and mutagenic properties but of course this is suspected. This class of compounds includes both nitrogen and sulfur mustards, epoxides such as diepoxybutane and epichlorohydrin and the alkyl sulfates and sulfonates such as diethyl sulfate and ethyl-methanesulfonate. Curiously, the alkyl sulfites, phosphates and phosphites are not mutagenic, perhaps because of their dipolar properties (Kolmark 1956). Hydrogen peroxide which is produced in the course of metabolism is weakly mutagenic and may act by producing organic peroxides (Dickey *et al.* 1949).

The alkylating agents are capable of reacting with DNA either to give triesters (Stacey *et al.* 1958) or by directly alkylating the purine or pyrimidine ring (Lawley 1957). The alkylated DNA then slowly hydrolyzes. Although the alkylating agents react with many compounds, it does seem that their mutagenic action occurs as a result of the reaction with the DNA. Loveless (1959) has shown that diethyl sulfate and ethylmethanesulfonate produce mutations of bacteriophage T2 when the phage is treated extracellularly with the alkylating agent after which the treated phages are used to infect bacteria. The ethylating agents were unique among the alkylating agents tested in their ability to produce phage mutations in this way. Since the major portion of the phage material which enters the bacterium is DNA, it is reasonable to suppose that the mutagen has reacted with this DNA to produce a stable, mutant DNA. Loveless (*l.c.*) points out the analogy between this phenomenon and the mutagenic effect of incorporated bromouracil in phage.

There is evidence for specificity in the mutagenic action of the

TABLE 10.   *Chemical Mutagens**

MUTAGEN	CHEMICAL FORMULA	MUTATIONS PER 10^6 CONIDIA (NEUROSPORA) IN THE BACK MUTATION TEST UNDER OPTIMAL CONDITIONS
Diepoxybutane	H_2C———CH—CH———CH_2 (with O bridges)	85
Dimethyl sulfate	$(CH_3)_2SO_4$	64
Epichlorohydrin	H_2C———CH—CH_2Cl (with O bridge)	56
Chloroethyl methane sulfonate	$ClCH_2CH_2 \cdot O \cdot SO_2CH_3$	51
Propylenoxide	H_2C———CH—CH_3 (with O bridge)	21
Diethyl sulfate	$(C_2H_5)_2SO_4$	18
Ethyleneimine	H_2C———CH_2 (with NH bridge)	16
Hydrogen peroxide + formaldehyde	$H_2O_2 + HCHO$	4.3
Nitrogen mustard	H_3C—N—$(CH_2CH_2Cl)_2 \cdot HCl$	3.4
Tert butylhydroperoxide	$(CH_3)_3C$—O—OH	1.5
Hydrogen peroxide	H—O—O—H	0.4

*After Westergaard, Experientia, vol. 13, 1957.

TABLE 11.   *The Relative Specificity of Six Mutagens on the Double Mutant Inositolless (37401), Adenineless (38701)**

MUTAGEN †	MUTATIONS PER 10^6 CONIDIA		PROPORTION
	INOS$^+$	AD$^+$	AD$^+$/INOS$^+$
Ethylmethanesulfonate $CH_3CH_2OSO_2CH_3$	11.3	17.4	1.5
Ultraviolet light	7.1	3.5	0.5
Diethyl sulfate	4.3	16.8	4
Dimethyl sulfate	3.4	64.0	19
Chloroethylmethanesulfonate $ClCH_2CH_2OSO_2CH_3$	0.3	51.0	190
Diepoxybutane	0.2	89.0	445

* From Westergaard, Experientia, vol. 13, 1957.
† The mutagens are compared under optimal conditions.

different alkylating agents just as there is specificity in the action of the different base analogues. Certain alleles will back mutate more readily with one mutagen than with another and the relative effects differ from allele to allele (Table 11). This type of mutagen specificity is shown only for particular alleles; as Westergaard (1957a, b) points out it is not a property of the locus (*i.e.*, of the requirement for inositol or adenine) but of the allele; that is, it "depends upon how the gene was originally damaged." If it is assumed that the different mutagens will react at different rates with the four nucleotide bases, and that only a single base substitution is involved in the mutation, then it is possible to account for the specificity.

This specificity of the alkylating agents is shown only for the process of back mutation. One explanation is that only specific changes will cause a gene to revert to its original condition (or near to it) but that almost any change can lead to inactivation of a whole cistron (*l.c.*). There is also a specificity in the mutagenic action of the phenylalanine derivatives of the nitrogen mustards; the L- form is much more efficient as a mutagen (in the Neurospora back mutation test) than is the D- form. Evidently the target reaction of the mutagen must be with an optically active compound.

It has been suggested (Stacey *et al.* 1958) that certain of the difunctional alkylating agents act by cross-linking chains of DNA. Although this may be correct in some cases, only one of the two alkyl groups of a compound like diethyl sulfate can actually be transferred to another molecule (Suter 1944). If the reactions leading to mutagenesis are alkylations, then the mutagen can transfer only one alkyl group per molecule of utilized mutagen which in turn means that mutation can occur without the provision of cross links between different molecules.

Many of the alkylating agents and also compounds such as caffeine are active in inducing chromosome mutations, that is, chromosomal breaks, deletions and other aberrations (Levan 1951). The chromosomes are of such complicated structure that it is practically impossible to indicate the chemical site of action of the agent used as a result of studying the chromosomal aberration produced.

There is no reason to require that all the mutagenic agents should act by the same mechanism. Radiation for example produces free radicals and peroxides and it was supposed (and still is) that a common pathway may be involved in the action of radiation and chemical mutagens. At the present stage of our knowledge it is quite possible that the mono- and difunctional alkylating agents produce mutation by different mechanisms.

There are definite differences between the action of radiation and the mutagenic "mustards." Auerbach (1951) pointed out early in the investigation of chemical mutagens that these substances tended to produce mosaics—patches of mutant tissue in a wild type Drosophila background—indicating that an "unstable gene state" was produced as a result of the treatment which would not yield mutations until after several cell divisions. This type of effect was not noticed when radiation-induced mutations were studied.

IV. Mutagens with Complex Effects

In 1927 Muller showed that x-ray irradiation would result in the production of lethal mutations in Drosophila. The discovery was rapidly followed by Stadler's announcement (1928) of x-ray-induced mutagenesis in barley. X-rays belong to a class of radiations which produce ionizations when absorbed by matter. In the decade following Muller's discovery it was shown that all ionizing radiation was mutagenic, but before World War II it had not been satisfactorily demonstrated that any chemical substance was mutagenic. This apparent limitation of mutagens to physical agents led to the view that mutation was a purely physical process caused by the absorption of energy. The "target theory" of mutagenesis supposed that radiation acted directly, just as a bullet acts directly on a target (Lea 1955). The bullet in this case was the quantum of radiation, the target was identified with the gene and the hit was identified as ionization within the gene target. The theory was, and is, quite successful in accounting for the quantitative effects of radiation on both mutation and on the inactivation of microorganisms and there is no doubt that it describes a part, perhaps even a large part, of the biological effects of high energy radiation especially on dried biological material. The gene is identified with the target, the region within which ionization must occur in order to produce the effect (mutation) studied. Only ionization within the target produces an effect (according to the theory in its original form) but ionization anywhere within this target will produce the same effect. The probability of effect is either 0 or 1 and this probability changes instantaneously at the target boundaries. (This is a very extreme statement of the theory.)

Certain definite predictions result from these ideas. First, since there is a constant probability that any particular quantum will cause an ionization within the target, the yield of mutation should be strictly proportional to the dose. There should be no threshhold or minimum dose required to produce an effect; a graph of effect as a function of radiation dose should pass through the origin. This prediction is verified by experiment. There has been a great deal of study of this point because of its obvious implications for consideration of the effects of low level radiation. As far as mutation caused by ionizing radiation is concerned it does appear that the probability of effect is constant. The target theory also predicts that the yield per ionization should diminish in exponential fashion at high doses as the "target" is hit more than once. Since there are so many genes and the mutation rate is, in general, so low this point is never reached and the curve always appears linear. When the inactivation of microorganisms is studied a typical exponential curve is obtained.

A second and related prediction of the target theory is that the effect of radiation should be cumulative and the intensity at which a given dose is applied should not be important. (This prediction only applies to the class of gene mutations. There are reasons related to the processes of chromosome repair why there should be an effect of dose intensity on the production of abnormal chromosome forms, or chromosome aberrations as they are usually called.) The prediction of the cumulative, dose-independent effect of radiation on mutation is verified in general although there have been some important exceptions reported. Russell *et al.* (1959) have reported an effect of dose intensity on the production of mutations in both male and female mice. They point out that their experiments can still be interpreted on the basis of the target theory but their work does imply different practical consequences.

A third prediction of the target theory is that the efficiency, or mutations produced per ionization, should be greatest for those radiations with a low ion density such as the hard x-rays and should be lowest for radiations with high ion density such as the alpha particles. Once again the prediction only applies to the gene mutations; chromosome aberrations require more than one hit since at least two breaks must be produced for an inversion or translocation. Aberrations are therefore produced with greatest efficiency by the densely ionizing radiations. The reason for the low mutagenic efficiency of densely ionizing particles is that these radiations are more likely to produce several ionizations in each target thereby "wasting" ionization. This prediction has also been verified in a series of experiments (Lea 1955).

The size of the gene—or of the hypothetical target responsible for the lethal effect of radiation—can be calculated from the curve of inactivation effect as a function of dose. If radiation "bullets" are shot at random the probability of hitting a target will depend on the size of the target. The dose required to inactivate 63 per cent of a sample (or to give 37 per cent survival) is the essential datum required. This dose corresponds to a survival of e^{-1} and represents the dose required to give an *average* of one hit in each target. It will be recalled that in the Poisson distribution the number of cases with one event or more is given by $(1-e^{-1})$. For the inactivation of microorganisms there is a large population in which rare events (hits on a particular target) occur; the Poisson distribution is therefore applicable. It was found that the size of dry viruses calculated on the basis of their sensitivity to radiation agreed quite well with their size as determined by other methods. Estimates of gene size and also of gene number have been made using the target theory (Lea and Catcheside 1945) but the exact meaning of such calculations is difficult to assess.

Ultraviolet (UV) radiation is mutagenic. The physical difference between this radiation and the ionizing radiations is the absorption of UV radiation by molecules in contrast to the absorption of the energy by atoms in the case of the x-rays. Since molecules display specificity in their absorption it is theoretically possible to determine the absorption spectrum of a molecule responsible for a physiological effect by plotting efficiency in producing the effect as a function of the incident wavelength. Such *action spectra* have been determined with a number of organisms. It is generally considered (Chapter 2) that the action spectrum for mutation provides evidence that the absorbing molecule is nucleic acid. Wagner and Mitchell (1955) do show in their book that the position of the maximum efficiency of absorbed ultraviolet light differs from organism to organism. The position of the absorption maximum for chromosome aberrations in Tradescantia does approximate the nucleic acid absorption spectrum rather closely (Kirby-Smith and Craig 1957).

V. The Chemical Nature of the Mutation Process: The Mechanism of the Induction of Mutations by Radiation

There is biochemical evidence that the genetic material, DNA, is inert and does not participate in cell metabolism (*cf.* Swick *et al.* 1956). Protein and RNA exchange material with newly entered cellular constituents and are said to have a rapid "turnover." DNA on the other hand is uniquely stable; once it is formed it does not show "turnover" and isotope incorporated into the DNA will not exchange with other materials in the cell. Notwithstanding this fact of DNA stability it is evident that the newer picture of the molecular basis of mutation requires the intervention of chemical phenomena in the process of gene mutation. If mutation is an inherited change in the order of the four naturally occurring DNA bases and if the DNA molecule is stable and does not exchange materials with the rest of the cell, then the changed base order can only be permanently introduced at the time of gene reproduction. DNA synthesis is a chemical process (Kornberg 1957) and it should therefore be possible to show chemical effects on the mutation process.

Contrary to the predictions of the target theory, environmental conditions greatly modify the response of cells to radiation. The presence of oxygen has a large effect on the results of x-ray irradiation (Hollaender *et al.* 1951). Cells irradiated in an oxygen

102

atmosphere have more chromosome breaks; bacterial cultures grown and irradiated anaerobically are much more resistant than similar cultures grown and irradiated aerobically. A variety of reducing compounds containing —SH groups has been shown to lessen the effect of ionizing radiation when the compounds are added before the onset of irradiation and such substances as AET (S, β-aminoethylisothiuronium $\cdot$ Br $\cdot$ HBr) may have a practical importance in protecting against radiation effects (Hollaender and Kimball 1956). This type of finding makes it seem likely that at least a portion of the radiation effect occurs via free radicals such as HO_2. The fact that it is possible to protect from the effects of ionizing radiation with chemical compounds shows that time sufficient for chemical action must elapse between the absorption of the energy followed by ionization and the irrevocable fixation of the change.

There is good evidence for the participation of a series of chemical intermediates in UV-induced mutagenesis. Ordinarily in studying radiation effects on bacteria the bacteria are irradiated while suspended in some liquid medium. Some years ago Stone, Wyss and Haas (1947) demonstrated that mutations were also obtained if a complex medium was irradiated with UV and the bacteria were added after irradiation. For some reason this effect has not been studied for several years, but there is good evidence that the radiation acting on the complex medium produced both free radicals and organic peroxides which were the actual mutagens.

A second and very peculiar property of UV-induced effects is the ability of visible light (particularly in the blue and near UV region) to reverse a portion of the UV-induced effects. The ability of a UV-treated culture to be photoreactivated is stable for many hours if the culture is kept in buffer but the ability to be reactivated decreases rapidly when the culture is incubated in a medium permitting growth and metabolism. UV effects on a wide range of organisms are reversed by visible light and even the inactivation of isolated transforming principle by UV can be reversed by visible light if an E. coli extract is simultaneously present (Goodgal et al. 1957). The extract seems to contain a heat labile and heat stable component. In spite of a large amount of work since the announcement of the phenomenon by Kelner in 1949 the mechanism of photoreactivation is really not known (Jagger 1958).

Dose-effect curves as a result of UV irradiation are not linear since the rate of increase in effect is higher at higher radiation doses. This non-linearity of response may occur because UV has more than one effect on the cell. It produces mutations but it also acts to inhibit DNA synthesis. The time during which DNA synthesis is inhibited is longer with increasing UV doses. There is evidence that UV mutagenesis is a complex process and requires time for its completion (see below). The time is governed by a biological clock—the time required for the DNA to duplicate (Witkin 1956). At higher UV doses the time for DNA synthesis is disproportionately lengthened and there is more time for the mutations to be established. The non-linear curve is therefore the result of the action of two processes. Witkin (1959) has been able to make the UV dose-effect curve linear by treatment and incubation in non-mutagenic concentrations of caffeine. The caffeine inhibits DNA duplication long enough for the maximum mutation yield to be obtained at lower UV doses.

One method of studying the mechanism of radiation induced mutation is to determine the effects of UV-irradiation and of treatment with alkylating agents on the metabolic processes concerned with the synthesis of gene substituents. One of the first effects of UV-irradiation is an inhibition of DNA synthesis (Harold and Ziporin 1958a). This inhibition occurs at doses lower than those required to inhibit the synthesis of protein or of RNA. With carefully controlled doses of UV it has been possible to demonstrate an accumulation of deoxynucleotides following radiation; the accumulated materials then disappear (Kanazir and Errera 1956). Treatment with sulfur mustard has also been shown to inhibit DNA synthesis before protein or RNA syntheses are affected (Harold and Ziporin 1958b). The exact point at which DNA synthesis is inhibited is not known. It is known that protein synthesis of some sort is required for the resumption of DNA synthesis blocked by radiation or sulfur mustard. The demonstration is made using either the antibiotic chloramphenicol which blocks protein synthesis without affecting RNA or DNA synthesis or by using nutritional mutants which require both an amino acid and thymine (Harold and Ziporin 1958a). The thymine requirement permits control of DNA synthesis; the amino acid requirement permits control of protein synthesis. Incubation in a complete medium permits restoration of DNA synthesis after a period depending on the amount of radiation. In the absence of the required amino acid or in the presence of chloramphenicol, no DNA synthesis occurs before the restoration of protein synthesis by the

104

addition of amino acid or the removal of chloramphenicol. A major difficulty with studies of this type is that most of the cells studied are irreversibly inactivated, that is cannot give rise to colonies when they are plated on a nutrient agar medium. Even though the treated cells resume synthesis of DNA, cell division is blocked. The population studied is therefore abnormal.

This is not the only evidence that prior protein synthesis is required for DNA production. The synthesis of virus DNA by infected bacteria requires a preliminary stage of protein synthesis (Burton 1955). If chloramphenicol is added at the time of infection DNA synthesis will not occur; if the addition of chloramphenicol is delayed for some time after infection, DNA made in the presence of antibiotic is genetically effective even though it cannot be incorporated into complete phage particles until protein synthesis is resumed. It must also be remembered that Stent (1955) has shown that the bacteriophage particle becomes insensitive to P-32 decay shortly after infection of the bacterium, indicating the participation of a molecule that does not contain phosphorus in the process of reproduction.

One of the facts that has been recognized about bacterial mutation is that several cell divisions may be required before the mutant phenotype is expressed. Mutation to bacteriophage resistance, for example, is not completed until twelve or thirteen generations following treatment (Braun 1953). There is some real doubt whether there really are any "Zero point" mutations, that is mutations produced and expressed immediately following cell treatment and without the participation of metabolic processes. There have been reports of the occurrence of mutations in nondividing cells (Ryan 1955) but even in these cases there is always evidence that active metabolism is required for the mutation process (Ryan 1959). Solely as a matter of definition, there can be no mutation without DNA division. Since mutation is a heritable change, change in the structure of DNA must be subjected to the test of reproduction to determine its inherited nature.

It is a real question as to what does happen before mutations are detected following treatment with a mutagen. At least two processes must be distinguished. One is the process of phenotypic lag. Assume that a cell has 100 enzyme molecules and that as a result of gene mutation the cell loses its ability to make enzyme. Assume also that the amount of enzyme is far in excess of that needed for some cell growth. Even though no more enzyme is produced, the first generation will have about 50 molecules of enzyme per cell, the second 25 and the third 12. If the phenotypic response depends on sterilization by penicillin, even the third generation cells may be sterilized since they will initiate growth, having a few enzyme molecules left. A second mechanism for the lag might be that of a delayed mutation as a result of the production of an "unstable gene" due to treatment with a particular mutagen. In practice it is often difficult, if not impossible, to differentiate or to evaluate the contribution of each different type of process to the mutation lag effect. There are mechanisms based on nuclear segregation that will also account for a part of the delayed mutations (Witkin 1951).

Some order has been imposed on this situation by a series of investigations on a particular type of mutation in E. coli, namely the process of reverse mutation from auxotrophy to prototrophy. Witkin (1956) and Haas and Doudney (1957) have been able to show that the majority of reversions are established within one division following treatment with UV. A curious fact has emerged from these studies. When bacteria such as Salmonella or E. coli are grown on a medium rich in amino acids, that is, on the usual broth medium, they temporarily lose their capacity to make amino acids rapidly, using instead the material supplied in the medium. (This loss is not genetic—cultivation on a minimal medium results in restoration of the missing enzyme systems after a time.) If tryptophan-requiring strains grown in broth are washed, irradiated and plated on a minimal medium only a very few back mutants are obtained. If the bacteria are cultivated for an hour after irradiation on a medium containing broth (and tryptophan) many mutants are obtained but if cultivation is on a minimal medium containing tryptophan, only a few mutants are produced, even after subsequent incubation with broth (Table 12). The effective component of broth is a mixture of amino acids; no one amino acid is sufficient and the efficiency with which mutants are obtained increases as the mixture becomes more diverse. The amino acids are required for a process of protein synthesis which must take place within a certain time after the treatment with UV in order for the "fixation" of the maximum yield of mutations. Incubation of cells after treatment with low UV doses with chloramphenicol results in an irretrievable loss of the mutations. (It is not known what happens to these "lost" potential mutants.) Reversions are not obtained upon subsequent incubation in the absence of the antibiotic, even though the antibiotic results in no apparent decrease in the number of viable cells.

Incubation of cells in a medium containing the amino acid analogue tryptazan—which is incorporated by cells to give an "abnormal" protein and which permits nucleic acid synthesis (Brawerman and Ycas, 1957)—results in a much greater decrease in the number of mutants that can be obtained on subsequent incubation in a medium containing amino acids than does preliminary incubation in the absence of tryptophan (Schwartz and Strauss 1958). These experiments indicate that normal protein synthesis is required for the *production* rather than the expression of the reversions.

If ultraviolet-treated cells are incubated on medium which does not permit rapid protein synthesis (the cells used must have been grown on a complex medium for the reasons indicated above; cells grown on minimal medium can synthesize amino acids rapidly enough to bypass the requirement for exogenous material) there is a gradual loss of the ability of these cells to respond to amino acid supplementation with the production of mutations. There is also a close correlation between the ability of cells to be photo-

TABLE 12. *Effect of Post-irradiation Incubation on the Yield of Prototrophs**†

POST-ULTRAVIOLET TREATMENT ‡	VIABLE CELLS PLATED	MUTANTS/ PLATE	PROTO- TROPHS/10^6
None	4.6×10^6	3.3	0.72
(a) 1 hr. AA, no tryptophan	5.2×10^5	1.0	2
(b) As in (a), followed by an additional hour in AA plus tryptophan	7.7×10^5	97.6	127
(c) 1 hr. in AA plus tryptophan	6.3×10^5	126	200
(d) As in (c), plus an additional hour in fresh medium of the same composition	8.2×10^5	144	175
(e) 1 hr. in AA plus methyl tryptophan	3.8×10^5	6	16
(f) As in (e), but followed by an additional hour in AA plus tryptophan	5.9×10^5	96.6	164
(g) 1 hr. in AA plus tryptazan	7.0×10^5	0	0
(h) As in (g), but followed by an additional hour in AA plus tryptophan	5.7×10^5	11	19

* From Schwartz and Strauss, Nature, vol. 182, 1958.

† 6.1×10^8 Tryptophan-requiring *E. coli* per ml. were irradiated with ultraviolet to give a survival of 4.6×10^7 cells/ml (7 per cent).

‡ All treatments were in minimal medium C supplemented as indicated. **AA indicates the addition of a complex amino acid mixture.**

reactivated and the ability of chloramphenicol to prevent the appearance of mutations (Doudney and Haas 1959). Both processes decline at the same rate. The period during which photoreactivation can occur is longer in the absence of active metabolism and the "pre-mutated state" is more stable on incubation in buffer than in a minimal medium with an energy source. Haas and Doudney use the terms "mutation stabilization" and "mutation frequency decline" to describe the processes of fixation into the genome and decline on incubation. Prolonging the time required for DNA synthesis to occur also prolongs the time during which mutations can be stabilized.

It has been shown that incubation before irradiation with purines and pyrimidines increases the mutation frequency and that there is a correlation between the mutation fixation process and RNA synthesis. Doudney and Haas (1959) suggest that radiation acts on RNA precursors to produce a chemical mutagen—requiring protein synthesis for its stabilization—which is then incorporated into the genome by a process requiring RNA synthesis.

This requirement of protein synthesis for the fixation of mutations is related to the use of ultraviolet radiation as a mutagen and is not characteristic of the mutation process in general. There is very definite evidence that the mutations induced in bacteriophage by 5-bromouracil do *not* require protein synthesis. Synthesis of phage DNA does require preliminary protein synthesis but if chloramphenicol is added 10 minutes after infection, DNA synthesis continues even though the formation of new protein is inhibited. Bromouracil is mutagenic even when added with chloramphenicol. This is taken to indicate that the compound substitutes for thymine in the DNA and that "protein synthesis is not necessary in initiating the series of events leading to mutation by bromouracil" (Litman and Pardee 1959). Mutations induced by caffeine (see below) can also occur in the presence of chloramphenicol (Glass and Novick 1959).

Mutations induced by the alkylating agents diethyl sulfate and epichlorohydrin do not require immediate protein synthesis for their fixation (Strauss and Okubo 1960). The number of mutants obtained after ethyl sulfate treatment increases after incubation with the amino acid analogue tryptazan and an increase in mutation frequency is obtained after incubation with chloramphenicol. Protein synthesis is not required although there is evidence for the participation of some metabolic process.

Since a new DNA configuration must be duplicated before a mutation is established there is time for the intervention of metabolic processes in the mutation process in general. Interference with metabolic processes involved in nucleotide metabolism may result in mutation.

A number of purines which are *not* incorporated into nucleic acids have been shown to be mutagenic for bacteria, fungi and even (recently) for Drosophila (Andrew 1959). These mutagenic purines include caffeine, theophylline, paraxanthine and theobromine which are all N-methyl xanthines. Adenine is also mutagenic. The effects are not large; with caffeine the mutation rate is increased by a factor of about 10 and the experiments performed by Novick and Szilard (1951) were performed in a continuous culture apparatus in which the bacteriophage resistant mutant cells had an opportunity to accumulate. When non-continuous culture methods (batch cultures) were used it required very careful plating techniques to demonstrate the caffeine effect (Glass and Novick 1959). In Novick and Szilard's experiments, in which mutation to bacteriophage resistance was studied, thymine, 6-methyl uracil and 5-bromouracil were *not* mutagenic even at a concentration of 150 mg/ml.

The mutagenic effect of these purines can be counteracted by purine ribosides such as adenosine, which are therefore classed as "antimutagens" (Novick 1956). There is no reason why conditions such as anaerobiosis or compounds such as catalase, cysteine and mercaptoethylamine should not be called antimutagenic but there is an intuitive feeling that a substance like adenosine must act in a more specific manner. Adenosine will also lower the spontaneous mutation rate to bacteriophage resistance.

There is evidence that caffeine is not incorporated into the bacterial nucleic acid and in fact is not even metabolized by bacteria (Koch 1956). These mutagenic purines probably act as enzyme inhibitors and Koch and Lamont (1956) have shown that caffeine does inhibit some of the enzymes concerned with nucleic acid metabolism. Since we do not really know all the enzymes involved in DNA reproduction, the exact point or mode of action of the mutagens cannot be defined. It is interesting that caffeine can be formed from the naturally occurring hypoxanthine by treatment with (the mutagenic) dimethyl sulfate under mild conditions of pH and temperature.

The balance in the supply of the various DNA precursors may

also control the mutation frequency. If a thymine-requiring double mutant of *E. coli* is incubated in a medium deficient in thymine it is observed that the frequency of mutation from auxotrophy to prototrophy for the second nutritional requirement is greatly increased (Coughlin and Adelberg 1956). This increase in the number of mutants comes after incubation in the absence of thymine for very short periods and is specific for thymine deficiency (Kanazir 1958). Thymine-requiring mutants start to die off when incubated in the absence of thymine because of the RNA/DNA imbalance in the mutant cells (which can synthesize RNA but not DNA) (Cohen and Barner 1954). The maximum increase in the yield of mutations comes before the cell number starts to decrease because of this death. It seems possible that an imbalance in the supply of precursors may cause a labilization of the DNA molecule in some way and therefore lead to mutation. The structural basis of the labilization is completely unknown. It is tempting to suppose that processes of this sort could normally occur in the cell and it is always possible that "errors" in the insertion of particular nucleotides might occur during normal DNA duplication leading to the production of spontaneous mutations.

Most of this discussion of mutation has dealt with the problem or induced mutation. There are always a certain number of mutants appearing in any culture whose origin can not be explained. For want of a better term these are called "spontaneous mutants." They cannot be completely accounted for by natural radiation and must therefore arise by some process intrinsic to the organism. It is known that the mutation rates of different genes differ and it is also recognized that this mutation rate itself is under genetic control. This fact alone indicates that mutation must be a metabolic process (Wagner and Mitchell 1955) since we suppose that gene action is mediated by metabolic processes. The spontaneous mutation rate is higher at high temperatures and the mutagenic action of naturally occurring substances such as adenine and hydrogen peroxide has been demonstrated.

In the years immediately following Muller's demonstration of the mutagenic effect of high energy radiation it was assumed that the genetic material was in some way special and isolated from the metabolic processes of the organism. After the discovery of the "dynamic state" of living organisms this isolation seemed even more plausible since it appeared that the genetic material, DNA,

110

had a much lower rate of turnover than other cellular constituents, thereby confirming the idea of the "metabolic isolation" of the gene. Notwithstanding these facts it is now evident that gene change is subject to a particular and specific sort of environmental control. Mutation, whether induced by radiation or by chemical mutagens, is a chemical process since it represents a definite structural change within a molecule, and it may even be that the process of mutation requires a series of metabolic events for its completion. Finally, if mutation is a change in the DNA code and if the code is the sequence of nucleotides (which is still only a working hypothesis—not a fact) then processes such as transformation, transduction, gene conversion and other non-reciprocal recombination mechanisms are closely related to the mutation process.

Chapter Five

Nucleo-Cytoplasmic Relationships
and the Problem of Protein Synthesis

Genetic experiments indicate the role of the genes and hence of the nucleus in the determination of cell heredity. The nucleus is a conservative element and serves as the primary storehouse of the information or memory of the cell.* This is a primary reason for the general lack of interest by physiologists in this organelle (Mazia 1952). Most physiological and biochemical experiments are concerned with the short term effects of a wide variety of external conditions on living (or once living) systems. How the system arrived at its position at the beginning of the experiment is, in general, ignored. It is as difficult to design an experiment to show what the nucleus does as it is to design an experiment to show what genes do—probably because it is the same problem. All the geneticist can do is to compare a normal system with a system in which—it is hoped—only one gene has been changed. The difference between the two systems presumably represents the effects of the gene. A similar type of procedure is the stand-

* In spite of the fact that the non-chromosomal elements may play an important role in inheritance I do not intend to discuss the problems of "cytoplasmic inheritance."

ard method for the investigation of nuclear behavior. A normal cell is compared to one with its nucleus removed or substituted by a nucleus from a different system. This methodology is required because nuclear effects must be mediated by the cytoplasm.

I. *Studies on Isolated Nuclei*

It is possible to isolate cell nuclei and other biological particles and study their enzyme content (Allfrey 1959). In a typical experiment cells are suspended in an isotonic medium containing the proper salts and sucrose or some similar substance to maintain the osmotic pressure. The cells are then homogenized and the cell free mass is subjected to differential centrifugation in the cold. The nuclei, as the heaviest particles, sediment first, then come the mitochondria and finally the microsomes, consisting of the small ribonucleoprotein particles (ribosomes) along with the endoplasmic reticulum. A great deal of work has been done on the problems of cell fractionation, including the problems of assuring clean separations and minimizing the danger of leakage of constituents from the particles. In the case of nuclear isolations it is important to have calcium ion in the preparations. Nuclei can be prepared free of cytoplasmic constituents in an acid medium containing citric acid but this inactivates many of the enzymes. It is also possible to isolate nuclei in non-aqueous media by the Behrens procedure but this method extracts many of the lipid constituents.

With a few exceptions the investigations on isolated nuclei have yielded uninteresting results. Part of the problem is that there is no satisfactory test for the "normality" of the isolated nuclei. With mitochondria it is always possible to determine whether the particles still retain their capacity for oxidative phosphorylation but no such test is available for nuclei. Probably the nuclei are very easily damaged. This is indicated by the fact that it is not possible to transplant nuclei successfully once they have lost their cytoplasmic coat—no artificial suspension medium is known which permits nuclei to retain their "viability" (King and Briggs 1956).

One enzyme has been reliably reported to occur exclusively in the nucleus. This is the enzyme synthesizing the coenzyme DPN from ATP and nicotinic mononucleotide (Hogeboom and Schneider 1952, Morton 1958). A great number of enzymes have been reported as present to some degree in nuclear fractions but it is not always clear when this is due to contamination. Such processes as the Krebs tricarboxylic acid cycle cannot occur to a major extent in nuclei because of the absence of most of the necessary enzymes. Oxidative phosphorylation *as found in mitochondria* should not be possible because of the apparent absence of cytochrome c oxidase, cytochrome c and the cytochrome c reductases. On the other hand, important biochemical processes obviously occur in chromosomes and many of them must require an energy source. Nucleotides added to a suspension of calf thymus nuclei are not phosphorylated but the intranuclear nucleotides can be phosphorylated and the nuclear process is inhibited by cyanide, azide and dinitrophenol as with mitochondria. Free nucleotides are tenaciously held by thymus nuclei (isolated in sucrose) and can only be released by special treatment; once released they are not taken up again. There is an ATP generating mechanism in nuclei which differs in detail from that in mitochondria (Osawa *et al.* 1957) and in which the polynucleotides are involved as cofactors (Allfrey and Mirsky 1957).

If calf thymus nuclei are incubated with labeled amino acids in medium of the proper composition they incorporate these amino acids into protein (Allfrey, Mirsky and Osawa 1957). This incorporation appears to be a case of real protein synthesis. Fractionation of the nuclear proteins after incubation indicates that the histones (the basic proteins of the chromosomes) are relatively inert as far as the protein synthesis reaction is concerned and that the specific activity of the protein most closely associated with the DNA (in the fractionation method used) is high. In their investigations Allfrey and his co-workers demonstrated that DNA is required for the reaction but that there is no specificity in the type of DNA required. Once DNA is removed from the nucleus it can be replaced by denatured or partly degraded DNA, by RNA, but not by purines and pyrimidines or by nucleotides or dinucleotides. A recent report (Allfrey and Mirsky 1958) states that synthetic polyanions can be substituted for the DNA, indicating that the role of the DNA in the incorporation reaction may be to control the charge distribution in the nucleus. The particular base sequence in the nucleic acid used is apparently of no importance.

II. *Enucleation and Transplantation Experiments*

One of the reassuring facts of work in biology is the repeated demonstration that important facts can be uncovered by simple experiments provided the investigator selects the proper biological material to answer his questions. Does the nucleus act continually or does a "single act of determination" occur at some time after gene duplication in which gene copies of some sort are sent out into the cytoplasm? Are the potentialities of a differentiating organism determined by the nuclear or non-nuclear parts of the cell? What is the functional role of the nucleus?

Answers to these questions were obtained by Hämmerling (1953) using the unicellular alga, Acetabularia, as experimental material. This macroscopic single celled organism has a single nucleus contained in a rhizome, a long green stalk and a "cap" or "umbrella" which is formed at maturation. Several species are known and these can readily be distinguished by the shape of the umbrella. Enucleation experiments can be readily performed by cutting off that portion of the rhizoid containing the nucleus. Ordinarily the whole organism can regenerate non-nuclear portions. Can differentiation occur in the absence of a nucleus?

If the umbrella of an enucleated organism is cut off, a new one may or may not differentiate completely depending on the length of the stalk. If the stalk is relatively long, complete regeneration will ordinarily occur. Differentiation—the formation of a new umbrella—can therefore take place in the absence of the nucleus. Regeneration will occur repeatedly in an organism containing a nucleus. However, the capacity for regeneration in an enucleated stalk is quite limited. If the regenerated umbrella is removed, it is most unlikely that a new one will be regenerated. The easiest interpretation of this type of experiment is that the nucleus produces some substance essential in differentiation which is stored in the cytoplasm and is used up during the differentiation-regeneration process. This substance must either be produced continually or produced when the cytoplasmic concentration falls below a certain value. The nucleus does not have to divide to produce this material. The experiments therefore indicate that the nucleus is continually active.

There is cytochemical evidence for this idea. In many organisms the DNA content of individual nuclei remains relatively constant but the protein and RNA content can vary widely depending on physiological conditions (Alfert et al. 1955). Cells that are actively secreting contain nuclei that are larger in volume than those of non-secreting cells and this increase in volume is due mainly to changes in the amount of protein. The correlation of nuclear composition with secretory activity is also evidence for the continual metabolic activity of the nuclei of non-dividing cells.

If an Acetabularia plant has both umbrella and nucleus removed and then a nucleus from a different species is transplanted, will the umbrella produced be of the original type or of the type of the plant donating the nucleus? In a large number of experiments Hämmerling was able to show that whereas the first cap produced after the transplantation was likely to be intermediate in character or characteristic of the nucleus of the donor (depending upon the length of the stalk) cutting off the first regenerated umbrella leads to the differentiation of an umbrella which was of the type characteristic of the transplanted nucleus. (In all experiments in which nuclei are transplanted there is a carry-over of some donor cytoplasm along with the nucleus. In control experiments, however, it was shown that only transplants containing a nucleus have an effect.) Both types of experiments with Acetabularia therefore indicate that a morphogenetic substance (something which induces a particular sort of morphological development) is produced by the nucleus and is stored in the cytoplasm.

Acetabularia is a green plant and continues to photosynthesize even after the removal of the nucleus. During the regeneration of a cap in the absence of a nucleus there is definite protein synthesis; this synthesis may, at first, be even faster than in nucleate fragments but it does eventually decline (Brachet *et al.* 1955). The synthesis of RNA has been reported in anucleate fragments in studies using an isotope dilution technique (*l.c.*) but a recent report from the same laboratory has failed to confirm these findings (Naora *et al.* 1959). It is certainly clear that RNA synthesis occurs in the nucleus to a great extent. Removal of the nucleus in Acetabularia does not have an immediate effect on the rate of synthetic process but eventually these do decay; the cell without a nucleus has neither recorded history nor future.

Protozoan nuclei may also be removed and transferred and many experiments have been performed with amebas. The results of these experiments are similar to those with Acetabularia if the different physiological state of the two types of organism after enucleation is taken into account. The main immediate effect of enucleation in ameba is a loss of the power of locomotion and of the ability to ingest particulate food. Enucleate amebas are therefore starving; enucleate Acetabularia can photosynthesize and are therefore in a nutritionally adequate condition (Brachet 1957).

117

Enucleation of the ameba does have an effect on "general metabolism" but not before a lag period of several days. There are drastic effects on protein and nucleic acid synthesis caused by nuclear removal. In comparison to the nucleate part, the anucleate part shows a steady decrease in RNA content and shows a decrease with time of the ability to synthesize protein and to incorporate radioactive amino acids into protein. Some protein and RNA synthesis may occur in the cytoplasm.

RNA has long been suspected of playing an important role in protein synthesis, partly because of the proximity of regions rich in RNA to those engaged in active protein synthesis (Caspersson 1950). One hypothesis is that RNA carries the genetic information from the nucleus to the cytoplasm. The transfer of RNA from nucleus to cytoplasm can be demonstrated by the technique of autoradiography.

In one type of experiment, performed by Goldstein and Plaut (1955), amebas were labelled with P-32 by feeding on P-32 labeled Tetrahymena. Tetrahymena can be grown on a synthetic medium containing labeled phosphate in contrast to the ameba which requires particulate food. The constituents of amebas fed on labeled Tetrahymena are labeled with P-32. Labeled nuclei were removed from amebas and transferred to non-labeled organisms, both to animals containing a nucleus and to animals with their nucleus removed. P-32 was observed to move from the nucleus to the cytoplasm. Treatment of the organism with ribonuclease solubilized the migratory P-32 and this was taken as evidence that the migratory P-32 compound was RNA. When both an unlabeled and a labeled nucleus were present in the same cytoplasm the phosphorus moved into the cytoplasm but did not move from the cytoplasm into the unlabeled nucleus. RNA transfer is therefore a one-way affair although as Brachet (1957) points out the resolution of the methods may not be high enough to permit so definite a conclusion.

A second experiment was described by Zalokar (1958, 1959). Neurospora hyphae are allowed to grow on the grid of a Beams air driven ultracentrifuge of the type used in embryology for the stratification of sea urchin eggs. The hyphae are treated with tritiated leucine (a protein precursor) or with tritiated uridine (an RNA precursor) for short periods and are then centifuged. The structure of the hyphae is such that it acts as its own centrifuge tube, each septum contains a stratified collection of cell particulates in the order: large granules, nuclei, mitochondria, microsomes, supernatant and vacuoles. A variety of cytochemical tests has been applied to determine the actual identity of each layer. It is not necessary to destroy the integrity of the cell in order to obtain this stratification. Autoradiography following treatment with the tritiated precursors, centrifugation and fixation permits identification of the particulate fraction containing the label. Zalokar's pictures were very clear. The tritiated uridine—an RNA component— appeared *first* in the nucleus and then migrated to the microsomes; the tritium labeled leucine appeared first in the microsomes and then moved to other parts of the cell. RNA is therefore synthesized in the nucleus and can move to the cytoplasm but it is not excluded that some RNA may be synthesized in the cytoplasm.

III. *The Influence of the Cytoplasm on the Nucleus*

In all cases in which whole organisms are studied nuclear action is expressed via the cytoplasm. Many experiments show in turn that happenings in the nucleus are determined by the cytoplasm. In Acetabularia, reproduction is by means of spores. The nuclei of "old" plants divide and the nuclei migrate to the umbrella where spores are cut off. The condition of the cytoplasm determines when the nucleus will divide. Transplantation of a young nucleus to old cytoplasm leads to nuclear division whereas an old nucleus transferred to young cytoplasm (without a cap for example) does not divide.

A classic observation showing the effect of the cytoplasm on the nucleus was made by Boveri on chromosome diminution in the nematode roundworm, Ascaris (Stern 1954). The fertilized Ascaris egg contains only two chromosomes, one from each parent. During the first division into an upper and lower cell, chromosome segregation proceeds normally. During the second division the chromosomes in the lower cell divide normally. In the upper cell each long chromosome breaks up into many parts which behave like independent chromosomes (chromosome diminution). Boveri noticed that occasionally the first division resulted in four cells which were geometrically oriented in the three possible combinations: three upper cells and one lower, two upper cells and two lower and one upper cell and three lower. At the next division diminution always occurred in the upper cell(s); the chromosomes of the lower cells always divided in orthodox fashion. Similar

119

results were obtained after centrifugation of egg cells. Since in Ascaris the cytoplasm of the upper cells is derived from a particular region of the egg it was concluded that the fate of the nucleus is determined by the condition of the cytoplasm.

Refinements in the technique of enucleation and transplantation, especially the methods of dissociating tissues into single cells by means of the chelating agent ethylenediaminetetraacetic acid (EDTA, versene) and the proteolytic enzyme trypsin, have made it possible to answer a famous question of nuclear physiology: does the nucleus differentiate? (King and Briggs 1955, 1956). The structural and functional differentiation of cells during the development of a multicellular organism is obvious. On the other hand, the facts of mitosis and the concepts of genetics seem to require that all cells have the same number and kind of chromosomes (neglecting the fact that many of the cells of higher organisms do become polyploid —that is, have more than two chromosome sets). Since it is obvious that different kinds of cells do different things, many or most of which are under the control of enzyme systems, and since these enzyme systems are in turn under gene control, it is apparent that some sort of mechanism (which is expressed in differentiation) must be interposed between genic potentiality and genic action.

It is possible to devise a reasonable theoretical system which indicates how differentiation could occur in a system with all its genes active (Delbruck 1949). Imagine the following system:

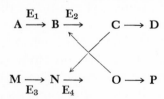

In the formulation A, B, C, D, M, N, O and P are substrates of the type encountered in metabolism and E_1, E_2, E_3 and E_4 are enzymes controlled by genes and catalyzing the reactions indicated. Suppose that substrate O inhibits the formation of C from B while substrate C in turn inhibits the formation of O from N. Such criss-cross inhibition is by no means a fantastic supposition; similar inhibitions probably play a role in controlling the rates of metabolic reactions (Chapter 1). Now assume that the system is balanced, one inhibition against the other, and that the final products D and P are produced at a steady rate. What will be the effect of any environmental perturbation that tends to increase

120

the rate of B $\longrightarrow$ C? A slightly increased amount of C will prevent the formation of some O which will lessen the inhibition and permit more C to be formed which will inhibit N $\longrightarrow$ O even more until the system switches itself over to the point where D is formed at an increased rate while P is hardly formed at all. Such a system will have irreversibly differentiated owing to a slight environmental change and without altering the distribution or the function of the genes or enzymes in any way. At the present stage of our understanding it is not really crucial that this mechanism should correspond to some real situation. The importance of such mechanisms is the demonstration that it is possible to have simple kinetic models for some of the complex phenomena of biology.

The question that King and Briggs have answered experimentally is related to these theoretical considerations. Is the nucleus of the differentiated cell itself differentiated or does it still retain all its genes (and other factors—if there are non-genetic nuclear factors) in working form? The historical statement of this question is: Is the nucleus of a differentiated cell totipotent? Some of the most noted biologists of the early twentieth century—Driesch, Loeb and Spemann—had shown that up to the sixteen cell stage any one nucleus carried all the factors required for normal differentiation, but until about 1955 it had been technically impossible to carry the analysis to a stage in which the nuclei were present in truly differentiated cells.

The design of the experiments that settled the question was as follows: Frog eggs were enucleated and then reinjected with nuclei obtained from the blastula, gastrula and from the neurula stage

TABLE 13. *Differentiation of Embryonic Nuclei (King and Briggs 1955)*

			DEVELOPMENT OF BLASTULAE		
SOURCE OF NUCLEI	NO. EGGS INJECTED WITH NUCLEI	COMPLETE BLASTULAE	ARRESTED BLASTULAE + GASTRULAE	ARRESTED NEURULAE + POSTNEURULAE	LARVAE (10–12 MM)
Animal hemisphere of early gastrulae	71 (100%)	29 (41%)	1	3	25
Chorda mesoderm of late gastrulae	83 (100%)	18 (22%)	8	8	2
Late gastrulae endoderm	67 (100%)	26 (40%)	8	13	5

Nuclei were obtained from cells treated with trypsin + versene.

of the frog embryo. The success of these transplants resulted from the development of a technique for separating undamaged neurula cells. Tissues may be separated into individual cells by treatment with versene and trypsin and this treatment greatly reduces the possibility of injury to the donor nucleus during its manipulation. Injected eggs which developed as far as the blastula stage—an indication of the success of the operation—were then scored for their ability to give complete embryos (Table 13). It quickly became obvious that the nuclei of the late gastrula stage are not totipotent since they do not support normal embryonic differentiation. Nuclei either differentiate or are differentiated during development. Furthermore, once the nuclei are differentiated they remain differentiated. Endoderm nuclei were transplanted into enucleated frog eggs, the eggs were allowed to develop to the blastula stage at which time the nuclei were removed and again transplanted to enucleated eggs. After the third serial transplantation the eggs were allowed to continue development. However there was no "rejuvenation" of the nuclei as a result of this serial treatment; development was still inhibited (King and Briggs 1956).

The fact of nuclear differentiation helps account for the production of tissue-specific enzymes (isozymes) (Markert and Möller 1959). It is known, for example, that the human prostate produces an alkaline phosphatase which is inhibited by tartrate in contrast to the enzyme in erythrocytes and this difference can be used for diagnostic purposes in cases of prostate cancer (Fishman *et al.* 1953). Markert has shown that different tissues can produce different proteins with the same catalytic properties. The exact meaning of the discovery is not clear but if genes control enzyme production some sort of nuclear differentiation would be necessary to account for the production of one type of enzyme protein in one tissue and a different protein in another.

IV. The Biochemical Mechanism of Protein Synthesis

The nuclear control of differentiation and the chemical processes that occur during differentiation are still outside the range of most biochemical methodology. However it is established that the genes control protein synthesis in some way and that the genes are located in the nucleus. The question that must be answered is "just how do genes control protein synthesis?" and in order to answer this question it is obviously essential to know how proteins are synthesized. There are at least two ways to approach this problem. One is by the stepwise procedure of biochemistry, identifying individual processes and isolating the individual synthetic systems. The second method is to attempt to study the characteristics of the protein synthesis reaction using the whole organism and to use such phenomena as *induced enzyme formation* to answer particular questions.

For many years it seemed as though the latter were the best approach; there was even some doubt expressed as to whether the methods of biochemistry as developed for the study of the reactions of intermediate metabolism would be adequate for the study of the biosynthesis of large polymers. Within the past few years such doubts have largely evaporated; the biochemical studies seem to be giving an answer while, as will be seen, the more biological methods give results that are often subject to a variety of ambiguous interpretations.

Protein synthesis appears to occur mostly in the microsome or small particle (ribosome) fraction of the cell (Zamecnik *et al.* 1956, Simkin and Work 1957). There are reports of protein synthesis by nuclei (Allfrey, Mirsky and Osawa 1957) and in Azobacter a protein synthesis reaction seems to occur in a system other than the small particles (Beljanski and Ochoa 1958) but in higher organisms and in some of the fungi (Zalokar 1958) the synthesis of protein seems to take place mainly in (or on) the small particles of the microsomes. The microsomes are actually rather heterogeneous; the small particles or ribosomes containing RNA + protein and the endothelial reticulum which is high in lipid material are both found in this fraction (Palade and Siekevitz 1956).

Protein synthesis is often measured by the incorporation of radioactive amino acids into the microsome fraction. The complete system contains a preparation of microsomes, two nucleotides (ATP and guanosine di- or triphosphate), "pH 5 enzyme" and salts and medium of the proper osmotic concentration. The "pH 5 enzyme" is a fraction precipitated from the supernatant fraction remaining after the removal of the microsomes by adjusting to pH 5 and collecting the precipitate (Hoagland *et al.* 1956). This fraction contains RNA—a soluble RNA not associated with particles (Hoagland *et al.* 1958). Although many other systems have been used, some of which will be discussed later, this system seems to be giving the most definitive answers.

There is evidence that the incorporation of amino acids into the microsomes represents true protein synthesis even though no net increase in the amount of protein is observed. The incorporated amino acids are linked by peptide bonds. Schweet *et al.* (1958b) have studied the incorporation of labeled amino acids into the microsomes of reticulocytes. The amino acids are incorporated into protein in a ratio characteristic of the composition of hemoglobin, the protein produced by these cells *in vivo*, and are not incorporated in the ratio of the total amino acids in the microsome protein. This indicates that a specific protein is being formed by the system. It is important to show that amino acid incorporation really represents protein synthesis since in some systems, such as those described by Gale and Folkes (1955), it was first thought that the process of amino acid incorporation could be dissociated from true protein synthesis although the processes were related. Real amino acid exchange with proteins *in vitro* probably has not been demonstrated (Gale *et al.* 1958, Simkin 1959).

The first process in protein synthesis consists of the activation of amino acids (Zamecnik *et al.* 1958). The process of peptide formation from free amino acids is not spontaneous and the amino acids must therefore be converted to compounds with a higher chemical potential. (The lengthening of peptide chains itself does not necessarily require large amounts of energy and can occur by the process known as *transpeptidation*. This process depends on a supply of peptides and can be catalyzed by the proteolytic enzymes. It is not known whether it has any physiological function (*cf.* Fruton and Simmonds 1958).) Since the amino acids contain both amino and carboxyl groups and since both types of groups can be activated it was not obvious *a priori* how the activation would take place. The evidence now is that activation occurs by reaction of the carboxyl groups of the amino acids. This was suspected because of the behavior of systems that form simple peptides and could therefore be considered as models for protein synthesis. Such systems are the synthesis of pantothenic acid from beta alanine and pantoic acid, the acetylation of sulfanilamide and the synthesis of the tripeptide glutathione. In all these syntheses it is the carboxyl group which is activated, either by combination with coenzyme A or by the formation of an adenylic acid derivative (Borsook 1956). At present it is believed that the initial reaction of protein synthesis is the combination of the constituent

124

amino acids with the biological energy transfer compound, adenosine triphosphate (ATP), to form an adenylic acid derivative of the amino acids in which the carboxyl group of the amino acid is combined with the adenyl portion of the ATP. The reaction may be written:

amino acid + ATP* ⇌ amino acid adenylate + pyrophosphate*

The asterisk indicates material labeled with P-32. In the presence of enzyme and amino acid, P-32 labeled ATP will exchange with non-labeled pyrophosphate. One evidence that this reaction is involved in protein synthesis is the demonstration that all twenty of the common amino acids can be activated (Lipman 1958); another is the behavior of certain analogues of tryptophan. Certain analogues of the amino acids are actually incorporated into protein. Sharon and Lipman (1957) demonstrated that those tryptophan analogues which were incorporated into protein were activated by the tryptophan activating enzyme. Those analogues which were not incorporated were not activated but instead inhibited enzyme action. This correlation indicates that the activation reaction is a part of the protein synthesis mechanism. Activation occurs in the soluble or supernatant fraction of the cell.

The second step in protein synthesis is a reaction of the amino acid adenylate to form an amino acid-RNA complex with a soluble RNA component which is present in the "pH 5 enzyme" complex (Hoagland *et al.* 1958). Both the first and second steps may be catalyzed by the same enzyme. The complex can be separated from the protein by standard procedures and a stable complex of labeled amino acid plus RNA can be obtained. The nature of this RNA is now being investigated in a number of laboratories

TABLE 14.   *Evidence for Specific RNA's in the pH 5 Enzyme: Additivity of Incorporation**

ADDITION	AMINO ACID INCORPORATED (INTO RNA-PH 5 ENZYME)
C^{14}-tyrosine	0.15
C^{14}-threonine	0.44
C^{14}-tyrosine + C^{14}-threonine	0.56
C^{14}-tyrosine + C^{12}-threonine	0.15
C^{14}-threonine + C^{12}-tyrosine	0.46

* Schweet *et al.*, Proc. Nat. Acad. Sci., vol. 44, 1958.

TABLE 15.   *Transfer of Leucine-C¹⁴ from Labeled pH 5 Enzyme Fraction to Microsome Protein**

	TOTAL C.P.M. IN	
	SOLUBLE RNA	MICROSOMAL PROTEIN
Before incubation—complete system	478	22
After incubation—complete system	182	433
Complete system minus GTP‡	116	67 †
Complete system minus GTP and nucleoside triphosphate generating system	62	101 †

* After Hoagland *et al.*, J. Biol. Chem., vol. 231, 1958.
† Indicates loss of label from intermediate without appearance in protein
‡ GTP = Guanosine triphosphate

and it is inevitable that this section will be out of date before it is printed. There is some evidence that there is a specific RNA component for each amino acid (Table 14) (Schweet *et al.* 1958a, Smith *et al.* 1959). If one saturates the RNA acceptor in the pH 5 system with threonine and then adds tyrosine there is additional incorporation, indicating that an RNA specific for the tyrosine has reacted. There seems to be agreement from a number of laboratories that the terminal nucleotides of the RNA acceptor are adenyl-cytidyl-cytidyl—and that the specificity for particular amino acids comes later in the molecule (*cf.* Hecht *et al.* 1959). The binding of the amino acids to RNA may be broken by treatment with ribonuclease or with dilute alkali.

The third step is a transfer from the soluble RNA to the microsome (Hoagland *et al.* 1958). It can be demonstrated with isolated RNA-amino acid complexes that guanosine triphosphate is essential for this transfer reaction (Table 15). Protein synthesis occurs after the amino acids are transferred to the microsomes.

V. Biological Studies on Protein Synthesis

So far this is the limit of the biochemical resolution of the mechanism of protein synthesis. Important biological questions still remain and there are several biochemical questions that arise in the consideration of the synthesis of a very large but highly specific macromolecule. The protein molecule is not a polymer in the same sense as is starch in which the number of repeating units is only one; in protein there are about twenty repeating units and these are arranged in a definite order. The number twenty has the attributes of a "magic number." According to Crick (1958) there are just twenty combinations of the four nucleotides which when taken three at a time without regard for order could select particular amino acids if only twenty of these were to be determined. According to these ideas, which may be outmoded already, amino acids such as hydroxyproline must have their hydroxy groups added after incorporation into the polypeptide chain.

One may ask two related questions: (a) are proteins synthesized via lower molecular weight intermediates in the stepwise fashion characteristic of intermediate metabolism and (b) how is specificity—both for linear amino acid order and three dimensional structure—imposed on the proteins? We would also like to know what is the relationship between the nucleic acids and protein synthesis? The hereditary material is DNA and there is the evidence obtained from genetic studies and by the method of P-32 decay (McFall, Pardee and Stent 1958) that the integrity of the DNA is important for protein synthesis. But there is (as will be seen) no evidence *as yet* that DNA is directly concerned with protein synthesis. There is evidence that RNA is made in the nucleus and transferred to the cytoplasm and we know that the small particles (on which protein synthesis occurs) are rich in RNA. What we would like to know is whether RNA is the carrier of the genetic information from nucleus to cytoplasm and particularly whether a *specific* RNA directs the formation of particular proteins?

One of the major tools for the investigation of these questions has been the phenomenon of induced enzyme synthesis in microorganisms. Certain enzymes such as penicillinase or beta galactosidase (lactase) will increase in amount on the addition of their substrates to the medium in which an organism is growing. It is not necessary that the *inducers* be acted upon by the enzymes they induce. Methyl-beta-D-thiogalactoside induces enzyme but is not split whereas phenyl-beta-D-galactoside is split by beta galactosidase but will not induce enzyme formation. The process of enzyme induction is complex and the mechanism is not understood but there are certain general characteristics (Pollock 1959). The process of induction represents true protein synthesis but it is likely that cells do produce a certain small amount of all the enzymes which can be induced even in the absence of exogenous inducer. The ability to produce enzyme is genetically controlled (Pardee *et al.* 1959)—recall the induction of the ability to use man-

127

TABLE 16. *Separability of Inducer Concentrating Process and Enzyme Induction**

ORGANISM	GROWTH ON LACTOSE	GALACTOSIDASE ACTIVITY		TMG † CONCENTRATION	
		INDUCED	UNINDUCED	INDUCED	UNINDUCED
Wild type K-12	Normal	1.78	Trace	1.85	Trace
Mutant type Lac$_1^-$	Very slow	1.09	Trace	Trace	Trace
Mutant type Lac$_4^-$	None	0.00	0.00	2.00	Trace

* From Monod, *in* Gaebler, Editor, Enzymes, Academic Press, Inc., 1956.
† TMG = methyl-β-D-thiogalactoside. TMG as % bacterial dry weight

nitol by a DNA transforming principle—but the actual enzyme production is determined by environmental conditions. In some cases "constitutive" strains are known which produce maximal amounts of enzyme without the addition of exogenous inducer: in these cases the properties of the enzyme produced by the constitutive strains are identical with those of the induced strain. Induction itself is a complex process, one system is required to concentrate inducer into the cell (the permease system) while the second leads to enzyme formation. These two systems are genetically separable (Table 16) (Monod 1956).

If one studies the development of lactase on a medium in which lactose is the sole carbon source an exponential curve of enzyme activity as a function of time characteristic of an autocatalytic reaction is obtained. The curve is the result of a complex of processes. As the ability to use lactose develops, the available amount of energy for general synthetic purposes increases and the ability to make more lactase increases. The process is self accelerating for this reason alone. Proper use of the induction phenomenon requires isolation of the process from other processes in the cell. In part this can be done by plotting amount of induced enzyme formed as a function of total cell mass or of total cell protein rather than as a function of time. A plot such as this isolates the increase in induced enzyme from the general processes of cell growth—that is, it provides a differential plot of the results.

The experimental method for the control of enzyme induction carries out the experiments in a condition of "gratuity," that is, under conditions in which the induced enzyme contributes nothing to the economy of the cell and may therefore be considered as a gratuitous constituent (Monod and Cohn 1952, Cohn 1957). For example if a non-utilizable inducer is added to a system in a

128

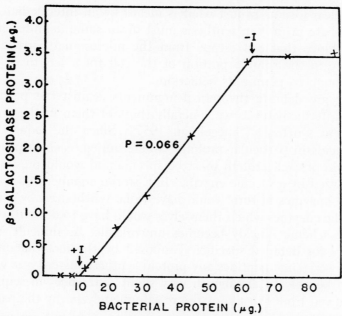

Figure 18. Gratuitous Induction of a Bacterial Enzyme. To a culture of ML 30 (lac +) growing exponentially on succinate-inorganic salts medium, methyl-β-D-thiogalactoside (I) was added at a concentration of 5×10^{-4} M. The enzyme activities measured were converted to μg of enzyme protein by using the value 3.36×10^2 μmoles/μg protein. At the point marked, $-I$, the inducer was effectively removed by adding 10^{-2} M phenyl-β-D-thiogalactoside, a competitive inhibitor of induction. For our purposes the addition of the inhibitor illustrates what would be seen if the inducer were removed by washing. Note that 6.6 per cent of the total bacterial protein is the induced enzyme itself. (Cohn, Bact. Rev., vol. 21, 1957.)

steady exponential state, enzyme will be formed from the time of addition (Fig. 18) but the enzyme will not contribute to the energy supply of the cell. When properly used, induced enzyme formation is a valuable method of controlling the synthesis of a specific protein—it is not necessary to study a general process of overall protein synthesis; one can study a specific synthesis using intact organisms.

VI. Intermediates in Protein Synthesis

The fact that the amino acids are transferred to the microsomes and that protein synthesis probably occurs on this particle argues against the role of free peptide intermediates in protein synthesis. In order to discuss the question more completely it is necessary to have a clear idea as to just what is meant by an intermediate. An intermediate in protein synthesis must mean some definite chemical substance that can escape from the microsomal particle and exist free in the soluble portion of the cell for a length of time long enough to permit its detection.

There are definite theoretical arguments against the participation of intermediates as we generally think of them in the process of protein synthesis (Spiegelman 1957). Since the sequence of amino acids in particular proteins is determined, each step in the formation of each protein must be specific and would presumably be catalyzed by a specific enzyme. But, so the argument goes, each of these enzymes in turn would have to be synthesized by a series of specific enzymes which themselves would have to be synthesized and the scheme quickly becomes unworkable. As difficult is the necessity for detailed specificity imposed by the fact that at the stage of very large peptides any protein synthesizing enzyme would have to be able to distinguish very slight differences in sequence far removed from the site of the reaction catalyzed by the particular enzyme.

An alternate hypothesis is therefore accepted by many biologists. It is envisioned that the constituent amino acids of any particular protein are lined up on a pattern or "template" and that the proteins are synthesized by the "simultaneous" polymerization of the constituent amino acids (or their activated derivatives) while on the template. We suppose a zipper-like polymerization starting at one end but schemes can be devised in which the polymerization starts at several points along the chain. There are two essential points to the hypothesis: First, free peptide intermediates do not occur and are not used as protein precursors—regardless of where condensation begins on the template none of the peptide elements are freed until the protein is completed. Secondly, the template material is specific for each particular protein; it is commonly supposed that the template material is RNA, obviously a specific RNA.

The removal of any one amino acid from a protein synthesizing system (by the use of analogues or by using nutritionally deficient mutants) results in a complete cessation of protein synthesis and of amino acid incorporation in microorganisms. (See the review by Spiegelman 1957.) Peptide fragments, not containing the missing amino acid, are either not formed or cannot be detected. If peptides are intermediates, and if only one amino acid is missing, one would expect the formation and accumulation of those peptides which do not contain the missing amino acid. On the other hand, the lack of accumulation is not really evidence. Accumulation, at or especially some steps behind the genetic block, is not an automatic thing but depends on the lack of reversible systems or of alternate pathways to take care of the accumulated substance. There are many nutritionally deficient mutants that do not seem to accumulate intermediates (Adelberg 1953).

If mammals are provided a meal lacking a single essential amino acid, feeding that amino acid several hours after the meal has no effect—the diet still is inadequate and is deficient in amino acids, indicating that the majority of amino acids will not form peptides which "wait" for the missing one in order to form protein (Geiger 1947). In bacteria requiring an amino acid (or uracil) there is no incorporation of any of the amino acids nor is there any induced enzyme synthesis until the missing amino acid is provided. Preventing the utilization of one amino acid suppresses the incorporation of all the others into peptide linkages. In the case of fluorophenylalanine, which may be incorporated into protein in some organisms, it was shown (with yeast) that there was no disappearance of glutamate from the free amino acid pool in the presence of analogue, indicating that the fluorophenylalanine had interfered with the uptake of amino acids which were not structurally related to the analogue (Halvorson and Spiegelman 1952).

The evidence however is not conclusive. There is evidence that RNA synthesis must accompany or precede protein synthesis. There is also evidence that a variety of the amino acids must be present for RNA synthesis to occur (Pardee and Prestidge 1956) (and it is possible to obtain RNA synthesis under conditions in which protein synthesis is not possible) (Gros and Gros 1958). The requirement for all the amino acids might be a requirement for RNA, not protein, formation. A technical detail which affects the interpretation of these experiments was demonstrated by Mandelstam (1957). Most of the tests to determine whether amino acid deficient mutants can form enzymes in the absence of their required growth substance are performed with the mutant suspended in a medium containing a carbohydrate or succinate as an energy source. Mandelstam showed that these conditions inhibit enzyme formation (under conditions of nitrogen starvation); in buffer, induced enzyme was formed in response to inducer even in the absence of the required amino acid. It is ap-

131

parent that there must be some sort of protein turnover; since it has been adequately demonstrated that induced enzyme formation represents true protein synthesis and is not "activation" of masked proteins, the amino acids required for the synthesis must have come from somewhere. But these experiments make it impossible to conclude that peptide intermediates are excluded because we do not know whether the turnover is at the amino acid or at the peptide level.

There are a series of elegant experiments on the induction of beta galactosidase and of penicillinase which make it very unlikely that there is any utilization of preformed peptide precursors in *growing* cells. Cells of *E. coli* were grown with either $S^{35}O_4$ as the sole sulfur source (Hogness *et al.* 1955) or with C-14 lactate as a sole carbon source (Rotman and Spiegelman 1954). As a result all of the constituents of the cell were uniformly labeled. The cells were then removed from the radioactive medium and suspended in medium not containing radioactive tracers and an enzyme inducer was added. After a short time in the growth medium containing inducer the cells were harvested and the newly induced enzyme was isolated and its radioactivity was determined. If the enzyme was radioactive it came, in part, from preexisting cellular constituents; if it was not radioactive it was formed *de novo*. In the case of beta galactosidase there is a specific precipitating antibody which aids in the enzyme purification.

The results of the experiments were quite conclusive. The newly formed enzyme did not contain a significant amount of radioactivity (1 per cent of the new beta galactosidase sulfur) even after a very slight increase in the amount of cell material (16 per cent). Similar results were obtained using C-14 lactate and Pollock has shown with penicillinase that it takes only about thirty seconds for cells of *B. cereus* in a complete medium to synthesize enzyme from the constituent amino acids (Pollock and Kramer 1958). (The results are particularly significant in view of the fact that in *E. coli* there is a substance serologically related to the galactozymase enzyme protein and this substance decreases in amount as the enzyme is formed (Cohn and Torriani 1952, 1953).) Therefore these enzymes are not formed in part from material originally present in the cell and there is no mass conversion of one protein into another. The results do *not* mean that there is no protein turnover in bacterial cells (as was originally thought) since the conditions of the experiment (rapid growth in adequate medium) are likely to inhibit or at any rate to mask the turnover which has been demonstrated under conditions of nitrogen starvation (Halvorson 1958a, b).

Suppose that there were a pool of peptide precursors in the cell and that these precursors could be incorporated into protein molecules. Suppose then that at a given time, t_0, a supply of a particular labeled amino acid was added. The amino acid would be expected to be incorporated into protein as would be the preformed peptide precursors. Now if it were possible to degrade protein molecules in stepwise fashion, isolate a particular amino acid from different parts of the protein molecule and compare the radioactivity of the same amino acid at different positions the results to be expected should depend on the type of synthetic mechanism. If peptide precursors play a role in protein synthesis one might expect to find differences in radioactivity since in some locations the particular amino acid would have been incorporated in the form of the non-labeled peptide presursor formed before t_0 while in other locations the amino acid would be incorporated in its radioactive form. Furthermore, the difference in the radioactivity of different positions of the protein molecule should diminish with time (after t_0) as the supply of precursors formed before t_0 is used up (Steinberg and Anfinson 1952).

The results of this type of experiment are contradictory. There is a uniform distribution of radioactivity in lactoglobulin, casein, aldolase, phosphorylase and glyceraldehyde-3-phosphate dehydrogenase after injection of amino acids into intact animals where net protein synthesis occurs (Steinberg and Mihalyi 1957). Valine injected into animals has the same specific activity either as an end group or in the inner portions of the hemoglobin peptide chain. The ratios of the specific activities of eight injected radioactive amino acids are the same in isolated crystalline aldolase and triose phosphate dehydrogenase (Simpson and Velick 1954) indicating that both proteins are formed from a common pool of precursors, most likely the amino acids. On the other hand in tissue minces or slices where net synthesis of protein is not observed a differential labeling of ovalbubin, ribonuclease and insulin has been obtained. It is therefore difficult to interpret the data (Steinberg et al. 1956). Perhaps the rate of synthesis is lower in the case of the slices and minces and there is time for exchange reactions to occur on the template. If the amino acids are hooked together in zipper-like fashion, then exchange might occur on the template at those positions not yet joined by peptide bonds. This model depends on the time required for protein synthesis and mimics the behavior of peptide intermediates.

The evidence for the existence of a template is reasonably good but it is obivously not complete. The reason for the definite preference for a template mechanism is that it is only this mechanism which seems reasonable in the light of what we know today about genetics and biochemistry .

VII. *The Role of Nucleic Acid*

In the last analysis we suppose that the specificity of the proteins is determined by DNA. And yet there is good evidence that DNA itself cannot be the template material. Protein synthesis occurs in enucleate Acetabularia. The major site of protein synthesis in most organisms is the small particle fraction of the cells —a region devoid of DNA. It is possible to dissociate protein synthesis from DNA synthesis; that is, inhibition of the *synthesis* of DNA by ultraviolet, x-ray irradiation, mitomycin (Sekiguchi and Takagi 1959, Shiba *et al.* 1959) or thymine starvation does not inhibit protein synthesis (Spiegelman 1957). (This last evidence which is often quoted does not really demonstrate the lack of a DNA effect since there is DNA present in these systems and it is not required that the template should increase.) Although DNA has been reported as necessary for amino acid incorporation by isolated thymus nuclei, the DNA may be replaced by other substances including synthetic polyelectrolytes (Allfrey and Mirsky 1958).

For many years biologists have assumed that RNA is the template material. In order to demonstrate this fact it must be shown that a specific RNA leads to the formation of a specific protein. The best demonstration of the hypothesis is the ability of tobacco mosaic virus RNA to direct the formation of a specific protein and of the RNA from certain animal viruses to infect and lead to the production of complete virus containing protein (Mountain and Alexander 1959, Sprunt *et al.* 1959). The most interesting report of a specific role of RNA in enzyme synthesis is that of Kramer and Straub (1957) on penicillinase formation which Pollock (1959) reports has been repeated in his laboratory. *B. cereus* cells were pretreated with ribonuclease and were then treated with a NaCl extract made from cells which are constitutive enzyme producers. The cells treated with extract produced large amounts

134

of penicillinase even though no penicillin was present in the extract. Treatment of the extract with ribonuclease abolished its effect.

There are many experiments which show that RNA *formation* must accompany protein formation. For example, although thymine-requiring bacteria can still form induced enzymes in the absence of growth factor (Cohen and Barner 1955), adenine- or uracil-requiring bacteria cannot. Inhibition of bacteria with the RNA analogue 5-hydroxyuridine inhibits formation of beta galactosidase (Spiegelman *et al.* 1955). In yeast, protein synthesis is inhibited on depletion of the pool of free nucleotides (*l.c.*). Gale (1956) and his colleagues have used an interesting preparation of sonically disintegrated staphylococcus cells for the study of protein synthesis. These preparations may be resolved for the study of the role of nucleic acids by treatment with nucleic acid hydrolases or by extraction with 1M NaCl. In the proper incubation mixture the cells can incorporate amino acids and synthesize enzymes although they have lost their capacity to divide. DNA is required for synthesis but it need only be added if 92 per cent of the endogenous DNA and 96 per cent of the RNA have been removed. In the system as studied, catalase formation responded only to the addition of intact RNA whereas galactoside synthesis by resolved preparations was stimulated by purines and pyrimidines but not by RNA. In all systems there is an inhibitory effect of ribonuclease treatment on protein synthesis (Brachet 1955). (This large molecule seems to penetrate many animal and plant cells with no difficulty in spite of what most of us have been taught to believe about permeability.)

Much of this type of work suffers from the difficulty that there is a lack of chemical identification of the different RNA preparations. We do not know the chemical nature of nuclear RNA, soluble RNA and the like. It is possible that determination of the structure of the specific RNA amino acid acceptors in the pH 5 enzyme fraction will help solve the problem.

Although protein formation (at any rate induced enzyme formation in microorganisms) seems to depend on RNA synthesis, the synthesis of RNA can occur in the absence of protein synthesis. Ochoa and his group (1957) have studied a bacterial enzyme (whose physiological role is unknown) which synthesizes an RNA from a mixture of nucleotide diphosphates. This polynucleotide phosphorylase synthesizes RNA with the same x-ray pattern as natural RNA but the composition of the synthetic material depends completely on the composition of the incubation medium; the enzyme will form a polyadenine when incubated with adenosine diphosphate. The antibiotic chloramphenicol will inhibit protein synthesis without inhibiting RNA synthesis in intact organisms as long as there is a supply of amino acids available (Pardee and Prestidge 1956). The RNA formed in the presence of chloramphenicol *in vivo* seems to be less stable than that formed in its absence but nonetheless it does seem to have the same base composition (Neidhardt and Gros 1957). It seems very reasonable to suppose that both RNA and protein are formed *in vivo* from a common precursor—perhaps something like the RNA-amino acids shown to be important for amino acid incorporation into proteins in the microsomes.

Although the experimental evidence supports the view that RNA or RNA synthesis is required for protein synthesis, except for the case of the RNA viruses and perhaps for penicillinase there is no demonstration of a correspondence between a specific RNA and a specific protein. It is not known whether concentration on the study of the inducible enzymes may have given a distorted picture of the whole of protein synthesis. The coding problem, the relationship between the postulated triads of nucleotides with particular amino acids on the template, has not been solved either in theory or in experiment.

The best supposition about the relationship between the genes, RNA and protein synthesis is that the DNA controls the production of a specific RNA which is sent out to the cytoplasm to direct specific protein synthesis. One of the curious facts about RNA and DNA composition is the difference in the base ratios of the various components when the RNA and DNA composition of various species is compared (Spirin *et al.* 1957). In twenty different organisms the ratio of guanine plus cytosine to adenine plus thymine varied from 0.45 to 2.73 in the DNA but the corresponding ratio of adenine plus uracil to guanine plus cytosine varied only from 0.99 to 1.013. If there were some direct correspondence between the RNA and the DNA one would expect a closer correlation between the base contents of the two compounds in different species unless there were two different types of RNA, only one originating within the nucleus. This idea of different types of RNA has been suggested before (Crick 1958) and there is now a reasonable amount of experimental evidence for the metabolic heterogeneity of RNA (Logan 1957, Hotta and Osawa 1958).

A direct relationship between a fraction of the RNA and DNA has been demonstrated by experiments done with bacteriophage and with yeast. There is no net synthesis of RNA in bacteria infected with bacteriophage but there is a rapid turnover of a fraction of the RNA of the cell following infection. The RNA synthesized subsequent to phage infection has a different nucleotide base ratio than the RNA of noninfected cells (Volkin *et al.* 1958). In fact the RNA formed has a composition equivalent to that of the phage DNA with uracil substituted for thymine. One possible interpretation is that the RNA serves as sort of a precursor or model for the DNA in a manner similar to that suggested by Stent (1958). The relationship has also been studied by Ycas and Vincent (1960). Yeast cells appear to form an RNA shortly after the addition of radioactive phosphate which has a base composition characteristic of the yeast DNA (with the uracil-thymine substitution) rather than that of the bulk RNA. These experiments are at least compatible with the idea of a direct base to base correspondence between RNA and DNA and with the idea that RNA is the chemical messenger from the genes to the protein synthesizing system. Certainly the experiments of Zalokar (1959) and of Goldstein and Plaut (1955) show that RNA can be formed in the nucleus and move to the cytoplasm.

The decisive evidence in support of these ideas is still missing. We do not know *how* DNA can form RNA containing specific messages, we do not know how the specific templates (one for each protein type) are formed or arranged and we can only be relatively certain that protein formation occurs on an RNA template at all.

Chapter Six

The Biochemical Genetics of Man

It *has* been demonstrated that genes control metabolic reactions by control of enzyme activity and it seems likely that the genetic control of enzyme activity is due, in part anyhow, to a control of protein structure. Our hypothesis is that the genes control protein structure by determination of the sequence of the amino acids in polypeptide chains. These ideas are as applicable to man as to the laboratory organisms used ·in most of the studies discussed. We should therefore be able to predict some of the expected effects of gene mutation in man.

A genetic effect on one of the single step reactions would cause a genetic block in one of the pathways of intermediary metabolism. This might result in failure to produce some necessary intermediate and/or the accumulation of some intermediate (or a derivative). The accumulated product might be toxic and it might also be excreted in large quantities to give a changed urine composition. Human abnormalities resulting from this type of change are called "inborn errors of metabolism," a term invented and popularized by the great English physician Garrod (1902, 1909). But not all genetic diseases which result in the excretion of large quantities of metabolic intermediates need be inborn errors of metabolism. Structural changes in the kidney might result in the excretion of large quantities of material: the condition would mimic an inborn error of metabolism but it would not be caused by a genetic block in a reaction of intermediary metabolism.

Genetic change, leading (as we suppose) to a change in the amino acid sequence of some protein, would probably result in the production of a molecule with changed physical or chemical properties. Ordinarily we would not be directly aware of the properties of the protein. If the change should occur in a structural or muscle protein or in some material present in large amount the changed protein would be noticed. In this type of case we can speak of "molecular disease," using the terminology devised by Pauling *et al.* (1949) for the discussion of sickle cell anemia. In the last analysis all inborn errors of metabolism are molecular diseases.

There is a major practical distinction between studies of the biochemical genetics of man and studies with other organisms. With human conditions and with human disease each individual is important—first for reasons of our ethos and secondly because we are not dealing with the large numbers of mutant organisms possible in the case of laboratory studies; rather we deal with single large organisms. There is a natural demand for the amelioration of symptoms by persons carrying the mutant genes and their progenitors and there is often the problem of genetic counseling: predicting the possibility of mutant offspring. This last problem requires good methods for the detection of heterozygotes, or carriers.

I. The Biological Basis of Human Individuality

For the genetic investigation of metabolic disease, and particularly for the investigation of the effects of heterozygosity, we must be able to show that the variation occasioned by a particular gene change is outside the range of variation of the various "wild type" alleles present in the population along with an assortment of modifiers. This is difficult to do except in the most extreme cases. Just as the "clearcut" mutants are studied in preference to those of "leaky" character, so the easily defined metabolic diseases are most used as examples. The differences between individuals in natural populations are probably greater than the differences between individuals in the laboratory populations used for the study of genetics and we are therefore faced with a series of problems resulting from variations of gene expression in human populations that do not occur so often in laboratory studies.

Individuals differ, not only obviously in their appearance, but also in their chemical makeup. It seems unlikely that the antigenic composition and the steady state concentrations of the various metabolites of intermediary metabolism are actually identical in any two individuals. One of the most interesting investigations of these individual differences is the investigation of the "homograft reaction" (Medawar 1958, Lawrence 1959, Merrill 1959). It is a common surgical experience that tissue transplanted from one person to another will not "take"—that is, will not grow and blend in permanently with the tissues of the host. Skin can be transplanted successfully from one point on an animal (including man) to another position on the same animal; we call this type of transplantation an *autograft*. Autografts (in which the donor is also the recipient) are most often successful. A *homograft* is a transplantation in which the donor is of the same species as the recipient and the *homograft reaction* is "the train of events that almost invariably causes a homograft of living tissue to be rejected by its host" (Medawar 1958).

The simplest measurement in experiments of this type is the record of the time of survival of the graft. Using this method of measurement it is possible to show that the reaction is antigenic in nature although it (apparently) does not depend on circulating antibodies of the type with which we are most familiar. Even though soluble antibodies are not detected, there are a number of characteristics that resemble antigen-antibody reactions. There is a latent period before the inception of the reaction; a homograft may appear to be healthy and to grow for a considerable period, but after a time it will become necrotic and die. The intensity of the reaction depends on the dose—the amounts of skin grafted— used to provoke it. The response is *not* local since the rejection of a homograft leaves its host in a sensitive state throughout the body, not just at the site of the original graft. Furthermore the sensitivity does not depend on which tissue has provoked the response —the antigens are not organ specific.

The nature of the antigens responsible for transplantation immunity is still unknown. The antigens can be obtained in cell extracts and at one time it was thought these substances were DNA-proteins (Billingham *et al.* 1956). Recent evidence indicates that although the antigen may be associated with DNA in the extracts, it is not a DNA-protein in any real sense. It is possible that amino acid-polysaccharides may be involved since the extracted antigens are destroyed by an enzyme which splits the blood group substances and these latter are known to be amino acid-polysaccharides (Medawar 1958).

The antigenic nature of the homograft reaction is the basis for the success of homografts in irradiated animals. It is well known that high energy radiation results in the inhibition of the ability of an organism to produce antibodies. Injection of a suspension of bone marrow cells, even from different species, into irradiated animals results in the establishment of these cells within the host and the production of erythrocytes containing cellular antigens characteristic of the cells injected (Bekkum and Vos 1957). The recipient organisms have become chimeras because of the successful transplantation, a result of inhibiting the antibody response.

There is a genetic basis for the homograft reaction and there have been a series of elegant investigations by Little, Snell and Bittner (Snell *et al.* 1953, Hoecker 1956) on the histocompatability genes in mice. Homografts will take when they are made between identical twins, between members of highly inbred lines or between the F 1 generation of a cross between two such highly inbred lines (Medawar 1958). Such transplants have been called *isografts* and behave like autografts. Occasionally, even at random, homografts will take and there is an increased time of survival when grafts are made between close relatives. The ability of the reacting mechanism to detect small differences is very marked. In some inbred strains transplants cannot be successfully made from males to females and the best analysis ascribes this difference to an antigen produced under the influence of the Y chromosome of the male (Eichwald and Silmser 1955). Estimates of the minimum number of genes responsible for the homograft reaction can be made by testing mutual compatibility in large series of animals. The analysis becomes very tedious but (depending on the analysis) the results show that *at least* 15 loci may be involved in some animals (Barnes and Krohn 1957).

The histocompatibility factors are only one class of differences at the antigenic level. There are also the variety of familiar blood types. Not only are there the common A, B, O types and the much publicized Rh alleles (or perhaps pseudoallelic series) but there are other, lesser known but equally well established types such as the M and N alternatives (Wiener and Wexler 1958). The num-

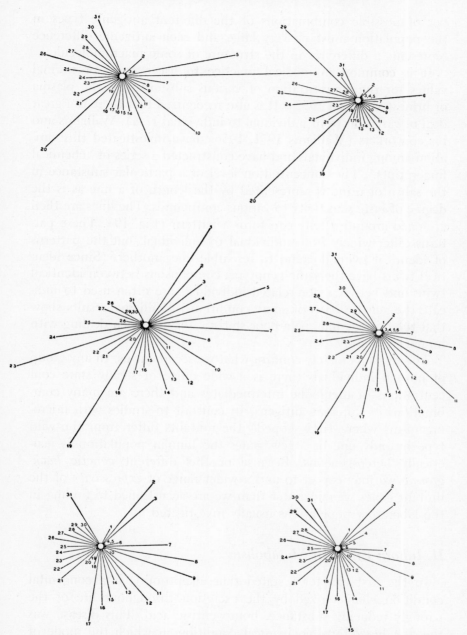

Figure 19. "Chemical fingerprints" from several individuals. The length of the lines represents the normal concentration of specific substances in the urine or the taste sensitivity to different substances. (Work done at the Clayton Foundation, University of Texas. Williams, Univ. Texas Publ., #5109: 1951.)

143

ber of possible combinations of the different antigenic types in the population must be very large and each antigenic difference represents a difference in the structure of some macromolecule.

It is common in medical practice to list average or normal values for the concentration of various substances in the plasma or urine (Albritton 1952). It is also recognized that there is a great deal of variation from individual to individual (*l.c.*). Williams and his co-workers (Williams 1951, 1956) have investigated this variation among individuals and have constructed a series of "chemical fingerprints." The concentration level of a particular substance in the saliva or urine is represented by the length of a line as is the degree of taste sensitivity to various compounds. The lines are then arranged around a center to form a pattern (Fig. 19). These patterns differ widely from individual to individual, but the patterns of identical twins do tend to resemble one another. (Since identical twins have the same genotype, comparisons between identical twins and between non-related individuals are often used to indicate the genetic basis of some condition.) Williams' results show that the average may be a poor statistic for use when dealing with humans clinically.

These results merely confirm what we see about us. In any group of normal individuals there is a wide range of steady state concentrations of metabolic intermediates and there are many combinations of different antigens. In contrast to studies with microorganisms where (it is hoped) the mutants differ from the wild type by only one or a few genes the human population is genetically heterogeneous. Because of this different *genetic background* we may expect to find a wider range of *expressivity* of the mutant genes we encounter than we are accustomed to finding in the laboratory populations usually investigated.

II. Inborn Errors of Metabolism

In the first chapter I stated that alkaptonuria is a congenital condition characterized by the excretion throughout life of the strongly reducing substance, homogentisic acid. This disease was the first hereditary biochemical condition in which the mode of inheritance was known. Garrod, in 1902, was the first to recognize that the condition represented a genetic block in intermediate metabolism. This was therefore the first real insight into the problems of chemical genetics (Knox 1958). Although I have stated earlier that Garrod's contribution had little influence upon the development of genetics, it did influence the concept of metabolism as a series of discrete steps. Sir Frederick Gowland Hopkins discusses the work of Garrod in terms that we might use today in his lecture on the Dynamic Side of Biochemistry given to the British Association in 1913 and there is no doubt that the demonstration of a definite intermediate in the metabolism of an amino acid played an important role in biochemistry.

The correspondence between this condition of man and the observations obtained much later with the biochemical mutants of the microorganisms is very close. We have pictured the genetic block as follows:

$$\text{Gene} \longrightarrow \quad \text{E}$$
$$\text{A} \longrightarrow \text{B} \left.\begin{array}{c} \\ \\ \end{array}\right\} \dashrightarrow \text{C} \longrightarrow \text{D}$$
$$\text{B}' \quad \text{Accumulate}$$

The picture obtained as a result of studies with alkaptonuria is very similar (Fig. 20). Homogentisic acid, an intermediate in the

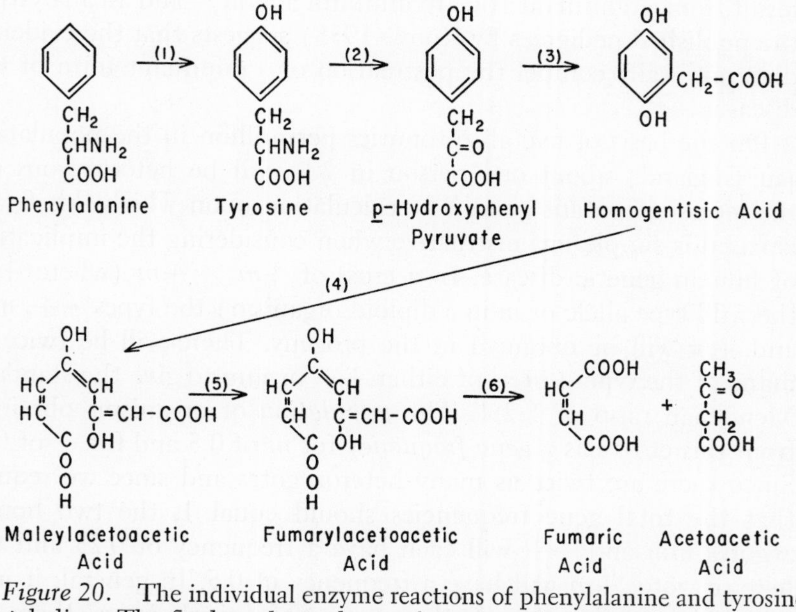

Figure 20. The individual enzyme reactions of phenylalanine and tyrosine metabolism. The final products shown, fumaric and acetoacetic acids, enter the tricarboxylic acid cycle. Reaction (4) is the one inactive in alkaptonuria. The enzymes catalyzing each reaction are: (1) phenylalanine hydroxylase; (2) tyrosine transaminase; (3) p-hydroxyphenylpyruvate oxidase; (4) homogentisate oxidase; (5) maleylacetoacetate cis-trans isomerase; and (6) fumarylacetoacetate hydrolase. (Knox, Am. J. Human Genet., vol. 10, 1958.)

145

oxidation of tyrosine, is excreted just as intermediates are excreted from a culture into the surrounding medium. The enzyme
catalyzing the blocked reaction is missing in the mutant organism,
that is, it could not be demonstrated in the liver of an alkaptonuric
patient (La Du *et al.* 1958). There is a Mendelian segregation of
a single gene and the condition results from the presence of two
doses of the mutant gene in the diploid. The method of genetic
investigation with man is different from the methods used with
laboratory organisms and it is necessary to draw conclusions from
much more limited data. In general, a single recessive gene is indicated when the condition does not occur in the parents or in the
offspring but does recur in the siblings of the affected individual.
Consanguinous marriage changes these expectations somewhat.
Hogben *et al.* (1932) have suggested that there may be two forms of
alkaptonuria, one the result of a dominant gene, that is, a form in
which the heterozygote displays the symptoms of the disease. It is
simpler to understand how a recessive gene would result in the loss
of enzyme activity—although of course it is possible for this action to
result from a dominant (due to inhibitor action)—and an analysis of
the published pedigrees by Knox (1958) suggests that the evidence
does not really compel the postulation of a dominant form of the
disease.

On the basis of five alkaptonurics per million in the population
(in England) about one person in 200 will be heterozygous for
the recessive mutant gene. The calculation upon which this figure
is based is simple but instructive when considering the implication
of human genetic disease. In a cross of $+m \times +m$ (where $+$ is
the wild type allele of m in a diploid organism) the types $++$, mm
and $+m$ will be obtained in the progeny. There will be twice as
many of the type $+m$ as of either $++$ or mm to give the standard
Mendelian ratio of 1:2:1. The *population* of organisms obtained
from this cross has a *gene frequency* for m of 0.5 and for $+$ of 0.5.
Since there are twice as many heterozygotes and since we require
that the total gene frequencies should equal 1, the two homozygotes mm and $++$ will each have a frequency of 0.25 and the
heterozygote, $+m$ will have a frequency of 0.5. In general, if in a
population (rather than in the progeny of a single cross) there are
two alleles m and $+$, and if we let p represent the frequency of one
allele and q represent the frequency of the other, the homozygotes
will have frequencies p^2 and q^2 while the heterozygotes will have the
frequency 2pq. These relationships are apparent when the alleles

have equal frequencies but in natural populations the frequencies of different alleles are most often not equal. If we assume a population in equilibrium—that is a population in which mating can be considered to occur at random and one in which there is either no selection against one of the alleles or one in which the selection is balanced by the net forward mutation rate—the relative frequencies of the homo- and heterozygotes are given by $p^2 + 2pq + q^2$ which is an expansion of the simple binomial $(p + q)^2$. By our definition of gene frequencies $p + q = 1$ and in situations when there are more than two alleles $p + q + r = 1$. The frequencies with which the various combinations occur in the population will be given by the expansion of $(p + q + r)^2$. This is perhaps the simplest sort of problem which is dealt with in a development of genetics known as population genetics. (See for example Li 1955.)

If the incidence of recessive alkaptonuria in the population is 5 per million this means that $q^2 = 5 \times 10^{-6}$ and q equals 2.24×10^{-3}. The frequency of q is so low that p is approximately equal to 1. The frequency of heterozygotes, 2pq, is then about 4.5×10^{-3} or about 1 in 200. This calculation has one very interesting consequence from the standpoint of human genetics. Since the greatest number of mutant alleles are carried by heterozygotes who do not have symptoms, preventing all the homozygotes from reproducing will not have an *immediate* appreciable influence on the frequency of homozygote production by the population.

The symptoms of alkaptonuria as they have been described are certainly not serious (although the psychological effects of the excretion of homogentisic acid may be great) and for some time it was supposed that the term "condition" was better than "disease." There are certain pathological symptoms. Patients over forty years of age often suffer from a pigmentation of the cartilages by a melanin-like substance (presumably a polymer of homogentisic acid); this discoloration was called "ochronosis" before its connection with alkaptonuria was discovered. A sufficient number of alkaptonurics develop arthritis to make it almost certain that there is a connection between the two.

Phenylketonuria is possibly the clearest example of a genetic disease of man with many similarities to the situation with microorganisms and with several interesting and unsolved aspects (Knox and Hsia 1957). In this disease there is an accumulation and excretion in the urine in quantity of phenylalanine and its pyruvic, lactic, acetic and acetylglutamine derivatives. The genetic block

147

TABLE 17.   *Incorporation of C-14 into Plasm Protein after the Administration of 3-C^{14}-DL-phenylalanine**

TIME AFTER EXPT. AD- MINISTRATION (HOURS)	PHENYLALANINE COUNTS/MIN/μM	TYROSINE COUNTS/MIN/μM	RATIO TYROSINE / PHENYL- ALANINE
Control (a)			
24	10.4	2.79	0.26
48	7.84	2.24	0.29
Control (b)			
24	24.6	4.90	0.20
48	21.0	4.70	0.22
Phenylketonuric (c)			
24	55.0	0.91	0.016
48	39.0	0.89	0.023
Phenylketonuric (d)			
24	46.0	0.70	0.016
48	33.0	0.69	0.021

* After Udenfriend & Bessman 1953.

is in the transformation of phenylalanine into tyrosine (Udenfriend and Bessman 1953). The enzymatic hydroxylation reaction is rather queer and involves two proteins, reduced DPNH and Fe^{++} ion. If oxidized DPN^+ is supplied, an alcohol or aldehyde must be added to the reaction mixture (Mitoma 1956). The reaction may be written:

$$\text{Phenylalanine} + \text{DPNH} + H^+ + O_2 \rightarrow \text{Tyrosine} + DPN^+ + H_2O$$

Of the two protein fractions fraction I is found only in liver and is very unstable; fraction II is found also in heart and kidney (*l.c.*).

Phenylketonurics are deficient in fraction I; activity of material obtained from the liver biopsy of a phenylketonuric patient was restored with fraction I obtained from the rat (Mitoma *et al.* 1957, Wallace *et al.* 1957). Both protein fractions are required even when DPNH is supplied, indicating either that the reaction is quite complex or that this is an interesting case of protein interaction similar to that reported for the tryptophan synthetase of *E. coli* (Crawford and Yanofsky 1958). It is possible that there is also an alternate pathway possible for the conversion of phenylalanine to tyrosine *in vivo* since a system containing ascorbic acid, Fe^{++} and O_2 can hydroxylate many aromatic compounds *in vitro*. The system might conceivably operate *in vivo*. There is evidence for a limited conversion of phenylalanine to tyrosine in phenylketonurics (Table 17) and patients are not completely deficient in the ability to make tyrosine.

The genetics of phenylketonuria is relatively straightforward and the disease is inherited as though it were controlled by a single recessive Mendelian gene. Studies of the genetics of this condition and of its distribution in populations are simplified because of the segregation of phenylketonurics in mental institutions. A mental defect is invariably associated with the disease. The gene frequency in Western populations is about 0.005, that is, about 1 out of every 100 persons is a heterozygote. Estimates of the gene frequency in Japan (Tanaka, unpublished) indicate a slightly lower frequency of about 0.003.

Several symptoms of the disease are not immediately related to the apparent position of the genetic block (Knox and Hsia 1957). There is an aminoaciduria accompanying the disease; smaller amounts of the derivatives of o-tyrosine and tryptophan such as o-hydroxylphenylacetate, indolacetate, p-hydroxyphenyl-lactate and -acetate can be detected by paper chromatography. An abnormal beta lipoprotein is detected in the serum. There are a variety of clinical signs. Phenylketonurics tend to have light pigmentation, there is a dermatological abnormality in many cases, one third to one quarter of the patients are epileptic.

There is a lack of correlation between the degree of mental deficiency—measured as an IQ—and the blood level or amount of phenylalanine and its derivatives excreted. Phenylketonurics differ widely in their intelligence and in some cases approach the normal range. There is also a wide range in the amount of intermediates excreted but the two phenomena are not connected. A phenylketonuric of relatively high intelligence may excrete as large quantities of phenylalanine and its derivatives as one of low intelligence. It is findings of this type that raise the problems of *penetrance* and *expressivity* in human genetics. Penetrance refers to the ability of a mutant gene to express itself. Pedigrees are recorded in which an individual very obviously must carry the factors for a genetic condition but displays no symptoms or at most very few. Expressivity refers to the possible variation in the degree of severity with which persons carrying genetic traits exhibit these traits. The difference between the terms is one of degree.

Nutritional mutants of microorganisms are defined as organisms that require the addition of some supplement to a basal minimal medium. Careful investigation often shows, even in the case of highly inbred Neurospora strains, that the quantitative requirement for the growth substance differs from segregant to segregant. In some cases there is a very large difference between segregants but in most of these cases it is possible to show the concomitant segregation of some other mutant gene which acts as a modifier or

149

suppressor. A number of these cases have been discussed in the preceding chapters. Since the metabolic step reactions are inter-related and since any one metabolic intermediate may be acted upon by several different enzyme systems which (we suppose) are under separate genetic control, it is not particularly surprising that other genes, the *genetic background*, may have an effect on the quantitative expression of the mutant gene which is being investi-gated. Findings of this type are not uncommon with laboratory organisms in which the genetic background is as uniform as can be had (although it is unlikely that any two strains derived from a common ancestor will retain genetic identity for many genera-tions). It is even less surprising that there should be wide variations in penetrance and expressivity in the genetically diverse popula-tions encountered in nature. And these ideas do not take into account the very large role of the environment on the modification of genetic potentiality.

The reverse side of the coin of penetrance and expressivity is the problem of *pleiotrophy*, the multiple effects possible from a single gene mutation. If gene action can be exclusively explained as due to control of the amino acid sequence of a single protein enzyme, how do we account for the multiple effects seen in a genetic disease such as phenylketonuria in which the single major biochemical lesion is accompanied by a series of minor biochemical abnormalities and of major clinical symptoms, all seemingly unre-lated? We suppose that just as the genetic background may have effects on a single mutant gene which are explicable on the basis of the interrelationships of the step reactions of metabolism, so the single mutant gene and its related single step reaction may have widespread effects on other metabolic steps. We have pre-viously analyzed the case of the succinate-requiring mutants of Neurospora (Strauss 1956) (Chapter 1) in which partially oxi-dized products of carbohydrate metabolism accumulate on the addition of a utilizable nitrogen source to a culture which cannot carry out one of the reactions of carbon dioxide fixation at the normal rate. The substances accumulated are not direct inter-mediates piling up behind the genetic block but rather are some-what removed from the metabolic pathway involved in the genetic lesion and accumulate because of metabolic interactions. Ob-viously we do not know the details of the mechanism resulting in multiple symptoms in phenylketonuria (or in many other of the genetic diseases) but there is no reason to doubt that the mecha-

150

nisms are the same as the mechanisms elucidated with the micro-organisms.

Part of the evidence that the symptoms of diseases such as phenylketonuria and galactosemia represent the effect of a single enzymatic deficiency is nutritional. Remission of the symptoms of the disease results from the removal of the precursor of the blocked reaction from the diet. If phenylketonuric infants are started on a special diet very low in phenylalanine there is an advance made by these children over those fed the usual diets (Knox and Hsia 1957). Even adults when put on a low phenylalanine diet show some improvement in the associated clinical signs although there is no good evidence of mental improvement in older persons. Limitation of phenylalanine in the diet results in a complete remission of *all* the abnormal biochemical symptoms which supports the single reaction hypothesis for the origin of the disease (*l.c.*).

The possibility of treatment of the symptoms of genetic disease is dramatically illustrated by a consideration of the rare congenital disease, galactosemia (Holzel *et al.* 1957). Persons suffering from this disease are unable to metabolize galactose in a normal manner. There is an excretion of galactose in the urine and an accumulation of galactose phosphate in the erythrocytes and probably in other tissues. There is also an excretion of larger quantities of amino acids in the urine (aminoaciduria) which commences a few days after the start of galactose feeding and ceases several days after the removal of galactose from the diet. The clinical effects of this disease are quite serious and include weight loss, enlargement of the liver and the development of cataracts. Untreated infants often do not survive. The major source of galactose in the diet is of course milk, since lactose on hydrolysis yields galactose.

Complete control of the disease may be achieved by the complete exclusion of all galactose from the diet; all lactose, milk, milk products and vitamin preparations compounded with lactose must be eliminated. A diet of egg, sugar, margarine and rice flour is prescribed for infants (*l.c.*). Galactolipids may be synthesized from glucose without the utilization of free galactose or of galactose phosphate as intermediates and the human can therefore tolerate a galactose free diet. As patients become older it is possible to add small quantities of milk or milk products to the diet (possibly because of the presence of an alternate pathway for galactose metabolism), but even then most patients indicate some discomfort attending the ingestion of milk.

151

It must be emphasized, regardless of how obvious it may seem, that such treatment of genetic disease ameliorates only the symptoms of the individual and does not change the character of the genes. The mutant genes in a treated individual will still be transmitted to offspring in their mutant form. Much nonsense has been written about the problems of eugenics and I do not want to do more than add my small addendum to this collection. Genetic traits are linked to other traits and the chance of an offspring suffering from a disease resulting from a recessive gene is low for most genetic disorders (assuming single gene inheritance) if the mate is chosen from the general population and is not also heterozygous. It is a question whether an alkaptonuric Einstein might not be as desirable an addition to the human race as a "normal" human being. This is one side of the picture—there are obviously other arguments.

Galactosemia has as its metabolic basis the absence of the enzyme phosphogalactose uridyl transferase (Anderson *et al.* 1957). Galactose is used structurally in the body in galactolipids—important materials in the construction of the nervous system and in membranes—and it is also metabolized, as are the other sugars, as an energy source. This metabolism requires the introduction of galactose into the usual metabolic pathways of carbohydrate metabolism which all seem to center around certain derivatives of glucose. The galactose must therefore be transformed into the glucose derivatives and this is done by a series of three enzymes (Kalckar 1957a). The galactose is first phosphorylated by ATP to form galactose-1-phosphate; the reaction is catalyzed by the enzyme galactokinase. Galactose phosphate then reacts with a glucose coenzyme derivative, uridine diphosphateglucose (abbreviated UDPG—the uridine diphosphate is a coenzyme in a number of reactions involving sugar derivatives) to form glucose-1-phosphate and UDPGalactose; this enzyme is given the unwieldy but descriptive name phosphogalactose uridyl transferase. Finally there is a reaction which reversibly transforms the UDPGalactose into UDPGlucose; this enzyme is called galactowaldenase or, recently, UDPGalactose-4-epimerase. The reactions are then:

(a) Galactose + ATP → Galactose-1-phosphate + ADP

(b) Galactose-1-phosphate + UDPG → Glucose-1-phosphate + UDPGalactose

(c) UDPGalactose ⇌ UDPGlucose

152

Since it is the UDP derivative that participates in transfer reactions the organism deficient in reaction (b) can make galactolipids from glucose without utilizing free galactose or galactosephosphate.

Galactosemics have no detectable phosphogalactose uridyl transferase in either their erythrocytes or liver (Kalckar *et al.* 1956) and they accumulate galactose phosphate in their erythrocytes. The genetic block in this disease is therefore at this enzymatic site. The lack of a particular enzyme is not the cause of the symptoms of the disease since these symptoms are relieved on a galactose free diet. The symptoms must therefore result from some toxic action of the accumulated galactose phosphate, from galactose itself or from some other related derivative (Holzel *et al.* 1957).

The aminoaciduria which accompanies the disease is probably of secondary origin. Sometime after galactose feeding begins there is an excretion of serine, glycine, alanine, threonine, glutamine and valine in amounts larger than usual. The problem with all conditions of aminoaciduria is whether the cause is metabolic, the result of an inborn metabolic error, or whether the disease is due to kidney malfunction. In galactosemia (and also in cystinuria which was used as one of the original examples of an "inborn error of metabolism") the excretion of amino acids seems to be renal in origin since the *plasma* levels of these amino acids are not abnormal as would be expected for metabolic disease.

III. *The Detection of Heterozygotes*

The clearcut biochemical nature of galactosemia makes it likely that the genetics is equally simple. For some time it was thought that the genetics was relatively complicated. I think it likely that the cause of the complication was the nature of the test used to recognize the heterozygote rather than the inherent nature of the disease itself. The problem of the detection of heterozygotes is related to the problem of the nature of dominance and it is useful to discuss it in some detail.

In phenylketonuria a simple phenylalanine tolerance test will invariably distinguish homozygous phenylketonurics from normal persons. The phenylketonuric will excrete phenylalanine (fed in the diet) as phenylalanine or as a derivative. It has also been established that phenylalanine tolerance is significantly lower in heterozygous individuals than in normal homozygotes and in addition that there is a higher plasma phenylalanine level in heterozygotes (Knox and

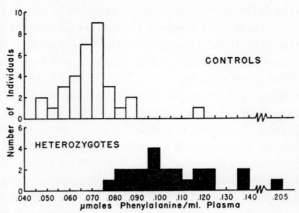

Figure 21. Distributions of plasma phenylalanine levels in 33 control and 23 heterozygous individuals. (Knox and Messinger, Am. J. Human Genet., vol. 10, 1958.)

Messinger 1958). If a series of normal and heterozygous individuals are classified by means of the tolerance test it turns out that most of the individuals can be separated into groups. There is a certain overlap and within this range it is not possible to distinguish between heterozygous and normal individuals (Fig. 21). (The figure illustrates a test based on plasma levels but the problems involved are the same.)

This type of result is almost to be expected from a tolerance test. The basic idea of this type of test is that the enzyme systems *in vivo* act at, or nearly at, full capacity. If the level of enzyme activity is reduced, the organism should not be able to metabolize any extra load of substrate. It is assumed in a phenylalanine tolerance test that the heterozygotes for phenylketonuria have less of an already saturated amount of the phenylalanine hydroxylase system than do normal homozygous individuals and they will therefore not be able to metabolize an extra amount of phenylalanine. The tolerance test will not work if enzymes are ordinarily produced in excess. If enzymes are present *in vivo* in two or three times the amount normally required, reducing the amount of enzyme by as much as one half will not raise the plasma level of any constituent and may or may not result in a lower tolerance test. If dominance occurs at a genetic rather than a metabolic level and if the amount of enzyme produced is not proportional to the gene dosage there will also be difficulty with the tolerance tests.

Regardless of whether tolerance tests work, it should be possible

154

to make classifications by actually determining enzyme activities in particular tissues. Even though the enzyme may do its major work in the liver or some other organ, it is most convenient for clinical purposes if the classification can be done with erythrocytes or whole blood; the galactose metabolic enzyme system is present to its greatest extent in the liver but it is much simpler to obtain erythrocytes for testing than it is to obtain a liver section.

Genetic classification in galactosemia is difficult to interpret when the galactose tolerance test is used as a basis for classification. There is a high incidence of abnormal galactose tolerance without clinical evidence of galactosemia among members of galactosemic families but abnormal tolerance cannot be shown in all cases in which the subject is presumably a heterozygote (Holzel et al. 1957). The difficulties are illustrated by the following pedigree. A female with an abnormal tolerance test but no clinical symptoms mated to a male with normal galactose tolerance had two sons who died in infancy from galactosemia and two daughters with abnormal tolerance but no symptoms of galactosemia (l.c.). One can either suppose that the father was a heterozygote with no penetrance or expression of the mutant gene or the pedigree can be explained on the basis of sex linkage (although there is no other evidence for this idea). The simplest interpretation is that the galactose tolerance test is affected by other modifiers so that it is not reliable for the classification of heterozygotes. A useful enzymatic assay was not obtained until recently when one was worked out based on the reduction of DPN (diphosphopyridine nucleotide) by a DPN linked UDPGlucose dehydrogenase (Bretthauer et al. 1959). The amount of UDPGlucose remaining in a reaction mixture can therefore be determined by measuring the enzymatic reduction of DPN after reaction with galactose phosphate has been allowed to occur. The reduction of DPN can easily be measured spectrophotometrically. In order for the test to give reasonable results the concentration of the various reactants must be adjusted carefully. Using this test, Bretthauer and his colleagues (l.c.) have shown that there are three classes of enzyme activity (Table 18). Galactosemics have no enzyme. Carriers or heterozygotes have an intermediate activity and although there is a range of activities, there does not seem to be an overlap between normals and carriers in the samples tested. There is no theoretical reason why an overlap should not be obtained even with this type of test. If genes control quantitative levels of en-

TABLE 18. *Transferase Activity in Erythrocytes**

		μM UPDGLUCOSE CONSUMED PER HOUR	
		PER ML. RED CELLS	PER GRAM HEMOGLOBIN
Mean:	Galactosemics	0	0
	Carriers	3.33	9.94
	Normal	6.14	19.0
Range:	Galactosemics	0	0
	Carriers	2.9–3.7	8.7–10.8
	Normal	4.8–8.1	14.7–25.4

* From Bretthauer *et al.*, Proc. Nat. Acad. Sci. U. S., vol. 45, 1959.

zyme activity by any direct or indirect mechanism, then the level of enzyme activity should be under the control of genetic modifiers and we might expect some sort of overlap at times. Overlap in an enzymatic test should occur more rarely than in the tolerance tests where there are several possible mechanisms which might result in overlap between heterozygotes and wild types. Bretthauer's data support the idea that galactosemia is the result of a single recessive Mendelian gene and they also support the idea that there is a close relationship between gene dosage and the amount of enzyme.

The detailed discussion of the inborn errors of metabolism has been restricted to alkaptonuria, phenylketonuria and galactosemia because it is these diseases which are the best known. As was pointed out above, it is often difficult to distinguish metabolic disease from structural disease which leads to deficiencies in amino acid reabsorption in the kidney tubules with a consequent aminoaciduria, as seems to be the case in cystinuria. A variety of metabolic diseases are known and their detailed description may be found in some recent books devoted to human chemical genetics (Hsia 1959, Harris 1955). One of the more interesting types of genetic disease is the condition of acatalasemia, a lack of catalase activity in the blood, reported in Japan. The disease, or condition, may be inherited as a single recessive Mendelian trait although there are some pedigrees that do not fit the description. The diagnostic test for heterozygotes is based on an enzymatic determination of catalase levels in the blood (Takahara *et al.* 1952).

IV. Molecular Disease

Presumably all the "inborn errors of metabolism" and indeed all genetic diseases represent molecular diseases since we suppose that genetic effects on metabolism or on anatomic structure are the end result of altered protein molecules. However, only in isolated cases are affected molecules produced in large enough numbers to permit their isolation and study from human material. In most cases the amount of the altered molecules is so small that it is the change in the catalytic property which is observed; the case in which an alteration in the protein itself has been observed is so far restricted to the anemias. An alteration in muscle protein would be a molecular disease that might have drastic effects because of changes in the mechanical properties of the protein. This might cause such a drastic effect that the condition would be lethal, that is, human organisms would not be able to go through a normal enough development to emerge into the world in even a tenuously viable condition. Embryonic death is one of the factors that probably prevents many cases of genetic disease from showing up. A "lethal" mutation in microorganisms can often be restored by adding growth factor but most serious effects in mammals will cause death *in utero*.

The best known cases of molecular disease in man are the hereditary anemias. Sickle cell anemia was discussed in the first chapter because the investigations of this condition have provided the only real evidence that genes control the amino acid sequence of proteins. It will be recalled that the sickling of abnormal erythrocytes is induced by a fall in oxygen tension and that sickle cell erythrocytes contain an unusual form of hemoglobin with valine substituted for glutamic acid at one position in the peptide chains (Ingram 1956). Nine different types of hemoglobin have been distinguished and all these hemoglobins have different properties (Table 19). Normal adult hemoglobin (A) and fetal hemoglobin (F) are found in all erythrocytes at some time but hemoglobin F disappears after birth. The abnormal hemoglobins now recognized are the sickle cell hemoglobin (S) and the hemoglobins C, D, E, G, H and I (Callender and O'Brien 1957). Although it is supposed that the lower solubility of hemoglobin S leads to tactoid formation and deformation of the erythrocyte with a consequent lowering of its life span, it is not really known if this is the correct explanation for the pathological effect of the amino acid substitution in the abnormal hemoglobins (Pauling 1954).

The genetics of the sickling conditions seems relatively simple (Neel 1951). The erythrocytes of heterozygotes will not normally sickle—only about 1 per cent of the erythrocytes are sickled in

157

TABLE 19. Physical and Chemical Properties of Hemoglobin Variants*

HEMOGLOBIN TYPE	ALKALI DENATURATION	RELATIVE MOBILITY ON PAPER ELECTROPHORESIS	ISO-ELECTRIC POINT	SOLUBILITY OF REDUCED HB	OXYGEN DISSOCIATION CURVE	ELECTROPHORETIC MOBILITY ($\times 10^{-6}$ CM²/VOLT/SEC)
HbA	Not resistant	2	6.87	Great	Normal	2.4
HbF	Resistant	3	7.0	>A	Abnormal	2.4
HbS	Not Resistant	4	7.09	Very Low	Normal	2.9
HbC	"	6	7.30	>A	Normal	3.2
HbD	"	4	7.09	=A	?	2.9
HbE	"	5	?	=A	?	Between A and S
HbG	"	3	6.98	=A	?	?
HbH	"	1	6.87	?	Normal	?
HbI	?	1	?	=A	?	1.7

* After Callender and O'Brien 1957.

the venous circulation—but they will sickle if the oxygen tension is artificially lowered. In the homozygous condition which results in anemia, 30 to 60 per cent of the erythrocytes in the venous circulation are sickled. An individual heterozygous for the sickle cell gene is said to have sickle cell trait but shows no amenia. Homozygous individuals are anemic. The available evidence suggests that the S and C hemoglobins are determined by alleles (Ranney *et al.* 1953) but of course this statement does not have the same operational meaning as similar statements made about laboratory organisms because there is little opportunity to determine the possibility of recombination. There is evidence (Schwartz *et al.* 1957) that hemoglobin G and hemoglobin S are determined by non-allelic genes since a pedigree has been described in which a parent carrying both G and S factors failed to transmit either to his son (Fig. 22).

Perhaps the best evidence for the allelism of the determiners for hemoglobins S and C is not genetic but rather functional (Table 20). Persons suffering from a doubly heterozygous hemoglobin disease—sickle cell hemoglobin C disease—produce both hemoglobin S and hemoglobin C but do not have any normal hemoglobin A. These individuals, and almost all persons with homozygous hemoglobin disease, produce some hemoglobin F. The reason for this production of fetal hemoglobin is not known. Since heterozygotes for a single factor produce both normal and abnormal hemoglobins it would be expected that a double heterozygote would produce three types of hemoglobin, normal and the

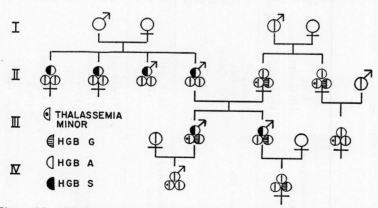

Figure 22. Thalassemia-hemoglobin disease. (Schwartz *et al.*, Blood, vol. 12, 1957; figure from Hsia, Inborn Errors of Metabolism, Year Book Publishers, 1959.)

TABLE 20. *Characteristics of the Common Abnormal Hemoglobin Syndromes**

	HEMOGLOBIN TYPES	SICKLING	ANEMIA	OSMOTIC FRAGILITY	RED CELL SURVIVAL
Single heterozygous syndromes					
Sickle cell trait	A(54–78) + S(22–46)	+	–	Normal	Normal
Hb C trait	A(56–72) + C(28–44)	–	–	May be decreased	Normal
Hb E trait	A + E	–	–	Normal	
Homozygous Hb disease					
Sickle cell anemia	S(60–100) + F(0–40)	+++	+++	Decreased	Greatly Reduced
Hb C disease	C(93–100) + F(0–7)	–	±	Decreased	Reduced
Hb E disease	E(92–100) + F(0–8)	–	±	Decreased	?
Double heterozygous Hb disease					
Sickle cell Hb C disease	S(35–63) + C(37–60) + F(0–7)	+	– to +++	Decreased	Reduced
Thalassemia syndromes					
Thalassemia major	A(10–90) + F(10–90)	–	+++	Greatly Decreased	Reduced
Thalassemia Hb S	S(60–81) + A(0–20) + F(0–20)	+	+++	Decreased	Reduced
Thalassemia Hb E	E(60–80) + F(20–40) + A?	–	+++	Decreased	Reduced

* After Callender and O'Brien 1957.

two altered types if the genes affected were not alleles. The fact that no normal hemoglobin is produced indicates that there is no "normal copy" of the information leading to hemoglobin A, that is, that the mutant genes are alleles. The fact that hemoglobins S and C have amino acid substitutions in the same position within the peptide chain may also be evidence for allelism although the reasoning here is somewhat circuitous. This is functional but not genetic evidence. There is no way of knowing whether the different diseases are analogous to the pseudoallelism found in other organisms or whether the fact that substitution occurs at just the same position in the peptide chain in hemoglobin S and C indicates that the mutations are at exactly the same location in the genetic fine structure. The chances that this point will ever be decided are, I think, relatively slight. The gene does not have the same operational meaning when we are dealing with man that it has when we are dealing with other organisms although there is no reason to believe that there is any fundamental difference.

The frequency of the sickle cell gene and of the hemoglobin C gene may be very high in certain populations. Measurements made in Africa indicate that certain tribes may show sickle cell trait in 40 per cent of the population. The frequency of the trait among Negroes in the United States is only about 9 per cent. Since any child who inherits two sickle cell genes from his parents will have a much lower chance of survival to reproductive age (about one fifth normal) one would expect a fraction (16 per cent) of the genes to be removed from the population in each generation. There must be some factor which contributes to the maintenance of the gene in African populations. Since new mutations would have to occur at too high a rate to account for the measured frequency it is likely that there is some positive advantage in having one dose of the sickle cell gene in certain environments, that is, that there is a selective advantage for sickle cell trait. This explanation seems to be correct. It has been shown (Allison 1954a, b, 1956) that the sickle cell trait in some way affords protection against malaria during the early years of life. The protection is great enough to maintain a high frequency of heterozygotes in spite of the semi-lethal nature of the gene in homozygous condition. When the selective pressure is removed (as in the United States where malaria is not a problem) only the disadvantageous effects of the gene manifest themselves and the gene can therefore

161

be expected to disappear from the population in a period of generations.

Thalassemia is a genetic disease which modifies the expression of the genes directly concerned with hemoglobin formation in a quantitative manner. In thalassemia major, the homozygous condition, there is a greatly increased production of hemoglobin F even in the adult and when a single dose of this mutant gene is present with the sickle cell gene (with which it is not allelic) it reverses the proportion of normal and sickle cell hemoglobin. The gene may be linked to the other conditions and it does act as a modifier of hemoglobin synthesis (Neel 1958). There is no information as to the mode of action of this modifier.

The heterozygotes in the abnormal hemoglobin conditions produce both types of gene products. There does not seem to be interaction between the alleles resulting in a modified or hybrid product nor does there seem to be any dominance at the level of these immediate gene products. The normal gene is phenotypically dominant, that is, heterozygotes do not display clinical symptoms, presumably because an excess of normal hemoglobin is produced. The evidence from the studies on galactosemia is that the heterozygote produces an intermediate amount of enzyme just as though enzyme production were proportional to the gene dosage (Bretthauer *et al.* 1959). Each gene appears to act independently of its partner on a homologous chromosome. Dominance in these cases is therefore not a feature or property of the genes but is instead a property of the rate at which the reactions controlled by the genes must occur in order for the normal functions of the organism to continue. Problems of dominance in galactosemia and sickle cell anemia are as removed from the immediate vicinity of gene function as are many—if not all—cases of the interaction of non-allelic genes.

There are varying amounts of abnormal hemoglobin in different heterozygous individuals (Table 20). There is no precise explanation for this difference in expressivity except to attribute it to some unknown action of the genetic background.

Kalckar (1957b) has suggested one interesting consequence of the problem of dominance for human genetics. The somatic cells of the organism are diploid and we expect that dominance relationships will be observed. The sperm cells and the egg cells are haploid and any mutant gene should exert its effect on these cells just as with the haploid microorganisms. Fructose is a major source of energy for sperm movement and we would expect genetic deficiencies in fructose metabolism to show up immediately in sperm—in fact it should theoretically be possible to classify sperm, or at any rate to select sperm, by taking advantage of the complete expression of genes in the haploid condition—assuming that there is no nuclear differentiation which prevents genes from acting in these particular cells.

V. A Program for Medical Genetics

Most writings on chemical genetics have stressed the advantages of microorganisms for the discovery of basic facts in this field. This emphasis has been necessary because of the reluctance of many persons to accept the validity of the comparative biological approach to human conditions—the idea that notwithstanding obvious differences organisms have more similarities than diversities. It should be clear by now that the principles of chemical genetics discovered with the microorganisms have validity—on the whole—for man. Just as interestingly (if without the practical importance) the principles discovered with man apply to the microorganisms. Perhaps it is this latter point which now needs emphasis. It has been demonstrated in these chapters that many of the most important discoveries in chemical genetics have been made in the first instance with human material. The first recognition of a genetic block came from Garrod's investigations on the human disease, alkaptonuria; the best and in fact the only evidence that genes determine amino acid sequence in proteins comes from studies on the hemoglobin variants of man and it seems quite possible to me that the problem of the nature of dominance and the relationship between gene dose and enzyme amount and action can be studied best with human material. Although it is not possible to obtain large numbers of genetically identical individuals, the human conditions are better studied. The wealth of clinical material probably provides many instances of genetically determined defects that would amply repay investigation.

I think it is possible to outline a perfectly rational program for studies in medical genetics and one may hope that departments of genetics in medical schools may become the rule rather than the exception. It is evident that biochemical studies will proceed in an effort to discover the bases and ameliorate the symptoms of genetic disease. This amelioration is possible, as has been demonstrated with galactosemia. There are analytical techniques which must be developed to permit adequate recognition of hetero- zygotes as an aid in genetic counseling and these methods can be used for study of the fundamental questions of the nature of dominance and of the activity of enzyme systems *in vivo*. Medical genetics does not restrict itself to the human but includes the study of the genetics of the parasitic disease vectors, animal and plant parasites, bacteria and viruses and requires a study of the genetic factors involved in the highly vexing problem of the de- velopment of resistance to insecticides and antibiotics. Probably methods also will be developed to study the genetics of somatic cells by means of the new tissue culture techniques. Studies of somatic recombination and of somatic mutation in such systems might yield evidence about the malignant transformation in cells. Finally the genetics departments must play an educational role in indicating to both physicians and to the public the role of genetic factors in disease and the possible methods by which man may make the best of his genetic inheritance in his changing environment.

References

Adams, Mark H., 1959. Bacteriophages. New York, Interscience Publishers, Inc.

Adelberg, A., 1953. The use of metabolically blocked organisms for the analysis of biosynthetic pathways. Bact. Rev. *17*:253–267.

Albritton, E. C., Editor, 1952. Standard Values in Blood. Philadelphia, W. B. Saunders Co.

Alexander, H., and Leidy, G., 1951. Determination of inherited traits of *H. influenzae* by desoxyribonucleic acid fractions isolated from type specific cells. J. Exper. Med. *93*:345–359.

Alfert, M., Bern, H. A., and Kahn, R. H., 1955. Hormonal influence on nuclear synthesis. IV. Karyometric and microspectrophotometric studies of rat thyroid nuclei in different functional states. Acta Anat. *23*:185–205.

Allfrey, Vincent, 1959. The Isolation of Subcellular Components. Brachet and Mirsky, Editors, The Cell. New York, Academic Press Inc., pp. 193–290.

Allfrey, V. G., and Mirsky, A. E., 1957. The role of deoxyribonucleic acid and other polynucleotides in ATP synthesis by isolated cell nuclei. Proc. Nat. Acad. Sci. U. S. *43*:589–598.

Ibid., 1958. Some effects of substituting the deoxyribonucleic acid of isolated nuclei with other polyelectrolytes. Proc. Nat. Acad. Sci. U. S. *44*:981–991.

Allfrey, V. G., Mirsky, A. E., and Osawa, S., 1957. Protein synthesis in isolated cell nuclei. J. Gen. Physiol. *40*:451–490.

Allison, A. C., 1954a. Protection afforded by sickle-cell traits against subtertian malarial infection. Brit. M. J., *1*:290–301.

Ibid., 1954b. The distribution of the sickle-cell trait in East Africa and elsewhere, and its apparent relationship to the incidence of subtertian malaria. Tr. Roy. Soc. Trop. Med. & Hyg. *48*:312–318.

Allison, A. C., 1956. The sickle-cell and haemoglobin-C genes in some African populations. Ann. Human Genet. *21*:67–89.

Anderson, E. P., Kalckar, H. M., and Isselbacher, K. J., 1957. Defect in uptake of galactose-1-phosphate into liver nucleotides in congenital galactosemia. Science *125*:113–114.

Andrew, L. E., 1959. The mutagenic activity of caffein in Drosophila. Am. Naturalist *93*:135–138.

REFERENCES

Aronoff, S., 1957. Photosynthesis. Botan. Rev. 23:65–107.

Auerbach, Charlotte, 1951. Problems in chemical mutagenesis. Cold Spring Harbor Symposia Quant. Biol. 16:199–213.

Auerbach, C., and Robson, J. M., 1946. Chemical production of mutations. Nature 157:302.

Avery, O. T., MacLeod, C. M., and McCarty, M., 1944. Studies on the chemical nature of the substance inducing transformation of pneumococcal types. Induction of transformation by a desoxyribonucleic acid fraction isolated from Pneumococcus Type III. J. Exper. Med. 79:137–158.

Barnes, A. D., and Krohn, P. L., 1957. The estimation of the number of histo-compatibility genes controlling the successful transplantation of normal skin in mice. Proc. Roy. Soc. London s.B 146:505–526.

Beadle, G. W., 1945. Biochemical genetics. Chem. Rev. 37:15–96.

Ibid., 1959. Genes and chemical reactions in Neurospora. Science 129:1715–1719.

Beadle, G. W., and Tatum, E. L., 1941. Genetic control of biochemical reactions in Neurospora. Proc. Nat. Acad. Sci. U. S. 27:499–506.

Beljanski, M., and Ochoa, S., 1958. Protein biosynthesis by a cell-free bacterial system. Proc. Nat. Acad. Sci. U. S. 44:494–501.

Bendich, A., Pahl, H. B., and Beiser, S. M., 1956. Chromatographic fractionation of deoxyribonucleic acid with special emphasis on the transforming factor of Pneumococcus. Cold Spring Harbor Symposia Quant. Biol. 21:31–48.

Benzer, S., 1957. The Elementary Units of Heredity in McElroy and Glass, Editors, The Chemical Basis of Heredity. Baltimore, Johns Hopkins Press, pp. 70–93.

Ibid., 1959. On the topology of the genetic fine structure. Proc. Nat. Acad. Sci. U. S. 45:1607–1620.

Billingham, R. E., Brent, L., and Medawar, P. B., 1956. The antigenic stimulus in transplantation immunity. Nature 178:514–519.

Bonner, D. M., Yanofsky, C., and Partridge, C. W. M., 1952. Incomplete genetic blocks in biochemical mutants of Neurospora. Proc. Nat. Acad. Sci. U. S. 38:25–34.

Borsook, H., 1956. The biosynthesis of peptides and proteins. J. Cell. & Comp. Physiol. 47 suppl. 1:35–80.

Brachet, J., 1955. Effects of ribonuclease on living root tip cells. Biochim. et biophys. acta 16:611–613.

Ibid., 1957. Biochemical Cytology. New York, Academic Press Inc.

Brachet, J., Chantrenne, H., and Vanderhaeghe, F., 1955. Biochemical interactions between the nucleus and cytoplasm in unicellular organisms. II. Acetabularia mediterranea. Biochim. et biophys. acta 18:544–563.

Bradley, S. G., 1958. Genetic analysis of segregants from heterokaryons of Streptomyces coelicolor. J. Bact. 76:464–470.

Braun, W., 1953. Bacterial Genetics. Philadelphia, W. B. Saunders Co.

Brawerman, G., and Ycas, M., 1957. Incorporation of the amino acid analog tryptazan into the protein of Escherichia coli. Arch. Biochem. 68:112–117.

Brenner, S., Benzer, S., and Barnett, L., 1958. Distribution of proflavin-induced mutations in the genetic fine structure. Nature 182:983–985.

Bretthauer, R. K., Hansen, R. G., Donnell, G., and Bergren, W. R., 1959. A procedure for detecting carriers of galactosemia. Proc. Nat. Acad. Sci. U. S. 45:328–331.

Brink, R. A., 1958. Paramutation at the R locus in maize. Cold Spring Harbor Symposia Quant. Biol. 23:379–391.

166

REFERENCES

Burton, K., 1955. The relationship between the synthesis of deoxyribonucleic acid and the synthesis of protein in the multiplication of bacteriophage T2. Biochem. J. *61*:473–483.

Callendar, S. T., and O'Brien, J. R. P., 1957. The Anaemias *in* Thompson and King, Editors, Biochemical Disorders in Human Disease. New York, Academic Press Inc.

Caspersson, T. O., 1950. Cell Growth and Cell Function. New York, W. W. Norton Company, Inc.

Chargaff, E., and Davidson, J. N., Editors, 1955. The Nucleic Acids. Chemistry and Biology. New York, Academic Press.

Cohen, S. S., and Barner, H. D., 1954. Studies on unbalanced growth in *Escherichia coli*. Proc. Nat. Acad. Sci. U. S. *40*:885–893.

Ibid., 1955. Enzymatic adaptation in a thymine-requiring strain of *Echerichia coli*. J. Bact. *69*:59–66.

Cohn, M., 1957. Contributions of studies on the beta-galactosidase of *Echerichia coli* to our understanding of enzyme synthesis. Bact. Rev. *21*:140–168.

Cohn, M., and Torriani, Anne-Marie, 1952. Immunochemical studies with the β-galactosidase and structurally related proteins of *Escherichia coli*. J. Immunol. *69*:471–491.

Ibid., 1953. The relationships in biosynthesis of the β-galactosidase and PZ proteins in *Escherichia coli*. Biochim. et biophys. acta *10*:280–289.

Colvin, J. R., Smith, D. B., and Cook, W. H., 1954. The microheterogeneity of proteins. Chem. Rev. *54*:687–711.

Corey, R. R., and Starr, M. P., 1957. Genetic transformation of colony type in *Xanthomonas phaseoli*. J. Bact. *74*:141–145.

Coughlin, C. A., and Adelberg, E. A., 1956. Bacterial mutation induced by thymine starvation. Nature *178*:531–532.

Crawford, I. P., and Yanofsky, C., 1958. On the separation of the tryptophan synthetase of *Escherichia coli* into two protein components. Proc. Nat. Acad. Sci. U. S. *44*:1161–1170.

Ibid., 1959. The formation of a new enzymatically active protein as a result of suppression. Proc. Nat. Acad. Sci. U. S. *45*:1280–1287.

Crick, F. H. C., 1958. On protein synthesis. Symposia Soc. Exper. Biol. *12*:138–163.

Davis, Bernard D., 1948. Isolation of biochemically deficient mutants of bacteria by penicillin. J. Am. Chem. Soc. *70*:4267.

DeBusk, A. G., 1956. Metabolic aspects of chemical genetics. Advances Enzymol. *17*:393–476.

Delbruck, M., 1949. Discussion following paper by Sonneborn and Beale, Influence des gènes, des plasmagènes et du milieu dans le determinisme des caractères antigèniques chez *Paramecium aurelia* (variete 4) in Unités biologiques douées de continuité génétique. Edition du Centre Nat. Rech. Sci. Paris, pp. 25–36.

Delbruck, M., and Luria, S. E., 1942. Interference between bacterial viruses I. Interference between two bacterial viruses acting upon the same host, and the mechanism of virus growth. Arch. Biochem. *1*:111–141.

Delbruck, M., and Stent, G., 1957. On the mechanism of DNA reproduction *in* McElroy and Glass, Editors, The Chemical Basis of Heredity. Baltimore, Johns Hopkins Press.

Demerec, M., and Hanson, J., 1951. Mutagenic action of manganous chloride. Cold Spring Harbor Symposia Quant. Biol. *16*:215–228.

Demerec, M., and Hartman, Z., 1956. Tryptophan mutants in *Salmonella*

167

typhimurium. Genetic studies with bacteria. Carnegie Inst. Wash. Publ., No. 612, pp. 5–53.

Dickey, F. H., Cleland, G. H., and Lotz, C., 1949. The role of organic peroxides in the induction of mutations. Proc. Nat. Acad. Sci. U. S. 35:581–585.

Dixon, M., 1949. Multi-enzyme Systems. London, Cambridge University Press.

Doermann, A. H., 1952. The intracellular growth of bacteriophages. I. Liberation of intracellular bacteriophage T4 by premature lysis with another phage or with cyanide. J. Gen. Physiol. 35:645–656.

Doty, P., Marmur, J., Eigner, J., and Schildkraut, C., 1960. Strand separation and specific recombination in deoxyribonucleic acids: Physical chemical studies. Proc. Nat. Acad. Sci. U. S. 46:461–476.

Doudney, C. O., and Haas, F. L., 1959. Mutation induction and macromolecular synthesis in bacteria. Proc. Nat. Acad. Sci. U. S. 45:709–722.

Eichwald, E. J., and Silmser, C. R., 1955. Transplantation Bull. 2:148–149.

Ellis, E. L., and Delbruck, M., 1939. The growth of bacteriophage. J. Gen. Physiol. 22:365–384.

Fincham, J. R. S., 1957. A modified glutamic dehydrogenase as a result of gene mutation in *Neurospora crassa*. Biochem. J. 65:721–728.

Ibid., 1958. The role of chromosomal loci in enzyme formation. Proc. Intern. Congr. Genet., 10th congr., Toronto 1:355–363.

Ibid., 1959. The biochemistry of genetic factors. Ann. Rev. Biochem. 28:343–364.

Fischer, G. A., 1957. The cleavage and synthesis of cystathionine in wild type and mutant strains of *Neurospora crassa*. Biochim. et biophys. acta. 25:50–55.

Fishman, W. H., Dart, R. M., Bonner, C. D., Leadbetter, W. F., Lerner, F., and Homburger, F., 1953. A new method for estimating serum acid phosphatase of prostatic origin applied to the clinical investigation of cancer of the prostate. J. Clin. Invest. 32:1034–44.

Fraenkel-Conrat, H., and Singer, B., 1957. Virus reconstitution II. Combination of protein and nucleic acid from different strains. Biochim. et biophys. acta 24:540–548.

Fraenkel-Conrat, H., Singer, B., and Williams, R. C., 1957. Infectivity of viral nucleic acid. Biochim. et biophys. acta 25:87–96.

Fraenkel-Conrat, H., and Williams, R. C., 1955. Reconstitution of active tobacco mosaic virus (TMV) from its inactive protein and nucleic acid components. Proc. Nat. Acad. Sci. U. S. 41:690–8.

Freese, E., 1959a. The specific mutagenic effect of base analogues on phage T4. J. Mol. Biol. 1:87–105.

Ibid., 1959b. The difference between spontaneous and base analogue induced mutations of phage T4. Proc. Nat. Acad. Sci. U. S. 45:622–633.

Fruton, J. S., and Simonds, S., 1958. General Biochemistry. ed. 2, New York, John Wiley and Sons.

Fuerst, C. R., and Stent, G., 1957. Inactivation of bacteria by decay of incorporated radioactive phosphorus. J. Gen. Physiol. 40:73–90.

Gale, E. F., 1956. Nucleic Acids and Enzyme Synthesis *in* Gaebler, Editor, Enzymes, Units of Biological Structure and Function. New York, Academic Press, Inc.

Gale, E. F., and Folkes, J. P., 1955. Assimilation of amino acids by bacteria XX. The incorporation of labelled amino acids by disrupted staphylococcal cells. Biochem. J. 59:661–675.

168

Gale, E. F., Shepherd, C. J., and Folkes, J. P., 1958. Incorporation of amino acids by disrupted staphylococcal cells. Nature *182*:592–595.

Garrod, A. E., 1902. The incidence of alkaptonuria: A study in chemical individuality. Lancet 2:1616–1620.

Ibid., 1909. Inborn Errors of Metabolism. London, Frowde, Hodder & Stoughton.

Geiger, E., 1947. Experiments with delayed supplementation of incomplete amino acid mixtures. J. Nutrition *34*:97–111.

Gierer, A., and Mundry, K. W., 1958. Production of mutants of tobacco mosaic virus by chemical alteration of its ribonucleic acid in vitro. Nature *182*:1457–58.

Gierer, A., and Schramm, G., 1956. The infectiousness of nucleic acid from tobacco mosaic virus. Nature *177*:702–3.

Giles, N. H., 1951. Studies on the mechanism of reversion in biochemical mutants of *Neurospora crassa*. Cold Spring Harbor Symposia Quant. Biol. *16*:283–313.

Ibid., 1958. Mutations at specific loci in *Neurospora*. Proc. Intern. Congr. Genet., 10th congr., Toronto *1*:261–279.

Giles, N. H., Partridge, C. W. H., and Nelson, N. J., 1957. The genetic control of adenylsuccinase in *Neurospora crassa*. Proc. Nat. Acad. Sci. U. S. *43*:305–317.

Gladner, J. A., and Laki, K., 1958. The active site of thrombin. J. Am. Chem. Soc. *80*:1263.

Glass, Elizabeth A., and Novick, A., 1959. Induction of mutation in chloramphenicol-inhibited bacteria. J. Bact. 77:10–16.

Glassman, Edward, and Mitchell, H. K., 1959. Mutants of *Drosophila melanogaster* deficient in xanthine dehydrogenase. Genetics *44*:153–162.

Goldschmidt, R. A., 1955. Theoretical Genetics. Berkeley, University of California Press.

Goldstein, L., and Plaut, W., 1955. Direct evidence for nuclear synthesis of cytoplasmic ribonucleic acid. Proc. Nat. Acad. Sci. U. S. *41*:874–880.

Goodgal, S. H., Rupert, C. S., and Herriott, R. M., 1957. Photoreactivation of *Hemophilus influenzae* Transforming Factor for Streptomycin Resistance by an Extract of *Escherichia coli B in* McElroy and Glass, Editors, The Chemical Basis of Heredity. Baltimore, Johns Hopkins Press.

Gorini, L., and Maas, W. K., 1957. The potential for the formation of a biosynthetic enzyme in *Escherichia coli*. Biochim. et biophys. acta *25*:208–209.

Green, D. E., and Järnefelt, J., 1959. Enzymes and biological organization. Perspectives in Biol. & Med. 2:163–184.

Green, M. M., 1957. Reverse mutation in Drosophila and the status of the particulate gene. Genetica 29:1–38.

Green, M. M., and Green, K. C., 1949. Crossing over between alleles at the lozenge locus in *Drosophila melanogaster*. Proc. Nat. Acad. Sci. U. S. *35*:586–591.

Griffith, Fred., 1928. The significance of Pneumococcal types. J. Hyg. *27*:113–159.

Grigg, G. W., 1952. Back mutation assay method in micro-organisms. Nature *169*:98–100.

Gros, F., and Gros, F., 1958. Role des acides amines dans la synthèse des acides nucléiques chez *Escherichia coli*. Exper. Cell Res. *14*:104–131.

Gross, D., and Tarver, H., 1955. Ethionine IV. The incorporation of ethionine into the proteins of Tetrahymena. J. Biol. Chem. *217*:169–182.

169

Haas, F. L., and Doudney, C. O., 1957. A relation of nucleic acid synthesis to radiation induced mutation frequency in bacteria. Proc. Nat. Acad. Sci. U. S. *43*:871–883.

Halvorson, H., 1958a. Intracellular protein and nucleic acid turnover in resting yeast cells. Biochim. et biophys. acta *27*:255–266.

Ibid., 1958b. Studies on protein and nucleic acid turnover in growing cultures of yeast. Biochim. et biophys. acta *27*:267–276.

Halvorson, H. O., and Spiegelman, S., 1952. The inhibition of amino acid formation by amino acid analogues. J. Bact. *64*:207–221.

Hammerling, J., 1953. Nucleo-cytoplasmic relationships in the development of *Acetabularia*. Internat. Rev. Cytol. *2*:475–498.

Harold, F. M., and Ziporin, Z. Z., 1958a. Synthesis of protein and of DNA in *Escherichia coli* irradiated with ultraviolet light. Biochim. et biophys. acta *29*:439–440.

Ibid., 1958b. The relationship between the synthesis of DNA and protein in *Escherichia coli* treated with sulfur mustard. Biochim. et biophys. acta *29*: 492–503.

Harris, H., 1955. An Introduction to Human Biochemical Genetics. Eugenics Laboratory Memoirs, London, Cambridge University Press, vol. 37.

Harris, J. I., Sanger, F., and Naughton, M. A., 1956. Species differences in insulin. Arch. Biochem. *65*:427–438.

Hartman, P., 1956. Linked loci in the control of consecutive steps in the primary pathway of histidine synthesis in *Salmonella typhimurium*. Genetic Studies with Bacteria, Carnegia Inst. Wash. Publ., no. 612, pp. 35–62.

Ibid., 1957. Transduction. A Comparative Review *in* McElroy and Glass, Editors, The Chemical Basis of Heredity. Baltimore, Johns Hopkins Press, pp. 408–462.

Haskins, F. H., and Mitchell, H. K., 1952. An example of the influence of modifying genes in *Neurospora*. Am. Naturalist *86*:231–238.

Hecht, L. I., Stephenson, M. L., and Zamecnik, P. C., 1959. Binding of amino acids to the end group of a soluble ribonucleic acid. Proc. Nat. Acad. Sci. U. S. *45*:505–518.

Herriott, R. M., 1951. Nucleic acid free T2 virus "ghosts" with specific biological action. J. Bact. *61*:752–754.

Hershey, A. D., 1955. An upper limit to the protein content of the germinal substance of bacteriophage T2. Virology *1*:108–127.

Ibid., 1957. Bacteriophages as genetic and biochemical systems. Advances Virus Res. *4*:25–61.

Hershey, A. D., and Chase, M., 1952. Independent functions of viral protein and nucleic acid in growth of bacteriophage. J. Gen. Physiol. *36*:39–56.

Hershey, A. D., Kamen, M. D., Kennedy, J. W., and Gest, H., 1951. The mortality of bacteriophage containing assimilated radioactive phosphorus. J. Gen. Physiol. *34*:305–319.

Hoagland, M. B., Keller, E. B., and Zamecnik, P. C., 1956. Enzymic carboxyl activation of amino acids. J. Biol. Chem. *218*:345–358.

Hoagland, M., Stephenson, M., Scott, J., Hecht, L., and Zamecnik, P., 1958. A soluble ribonucleic acid intermediate in protein synthesis. J. Biol. Chem. *231*:241–257.

Hoecker, G., 1956. Genetic mechanisms in tissue transplantation in the mouse. Cold Spring Harbor Symposia Quant. Biol. *21*:355–362.

Hogben, L., Worrall, R. L., and Zieve, I., 1932. The genetic basis of alkaptonuria. Proc. Roy. Soc. Edinburgh *B52*:264–295.

Hogeboom, G. H., and Schneider, W. C., 1952. Cytochemical Studies VI.

The synthesis of diphosphopyridine nucleotide by liver cell nuclei. J. Biol. Chem. *197*:611–620.

Hogness, D. S., Cohn, M., and Monad, J., 1955. Studies on the induced synthesis of beta-galactosidase in *Escherichia coli:* The kinetics and mechanism of sulfur incorporation. Biochim. et biophys. acta *16*:99–116.

Hollaender, A., Baker, W. K., and Anderson, E. H., 1951. Effect of oxygen tension and certain chemicals on the x-ray sensitivity of mutation production and survival. Cold Spring Harbor Symposia Quant. Biol. *16*:315–326.

Hollaender, A., and Kimball, R. F., 1956. Modification of radiation-induced genetic damage. Nature *177*:726–730.

Holzel, A., Komrower, G. M., and Schwarz, V., 1957. Galactosemia. Am. J. Med. *22*:703–711.

Hopkins, F. G., 1913. The Dynamic Side of Biochemistry *in* Needham and Baldwin, Editors, Hopkins and Biochemistry, Cambridge, Heffer and Sons.

Horowitz, N. H., 1956. Progress in developing chemical concepts of genetic phenomena. Fed. Proc. *15*:817–822.

Horowitz, N. H., and Fling, M., 1953. Genetic determination of tyrosinase thermostability in Neurospora. Genetics *38*:360–374.

Hotchkiss, R. D., 1954. Cyclical behavior in pneumococcal growth and transformability occasioned by environmental changes. Proc. Nat. Acad. Sci. U. S. *40*:49–55.

Ibid., 1955. The Biological Role of the Deoxypentose-Nucleic Acids *in* Chargaff and Davidson, Editors, The Nucleic Acids. New York, Academic Press, vol. 2.

Ibid., 1956. The Genetic Organization of the Deoxyribonucleate Units Functioning in Bacterial Transformation *in* Gaebler, Editor, Enzymes: Units of Biological Structure and Function. New York, Academic Press, Inc.

Hotta, Y., and Osawa, S., 1958. Nuclear and cytoplasmic ribonucleic acids. Biochim. et biophys. acta *28*:642–643.

Howard, A., and Pelc, S. R., 1951. Nuclear incorporation of P^{32} as demonstrated by autoradiographs. Exper. Cell Res. *11*:249–264.

Hsia, D. Y., 1959. Inborn Errors of Metabolism. Chicago, Year Book Publishers.

Hunt, J. A., and Ingram, V. M., 1958. Allelomorphism and the chemical differences of the human hemoglobins A, S and C. Nature *181*:1062–63.

Ingram, V. M., 1956. A specific chemical difference between the globins of normal human and sickle cell anemia hemoglobin. Nature *178*:792–794.

Jacob, F., and Wollman, E., 1955. Etude genetique d'un bacteriophage tempere d'*Escherichia coli*. III. Effect du rayonnemont ultraviolet sur la recombinaison genetique. Ann. Inst. Pasteur *88*:724–749.

Ibid., 1958. Genetic and physical determinations of chromosomal segments in *Escherichia coli*. Symposia Soc. Exper. Biol. *11*:75–92.

Jagger, J., 1958. Photoreactivation. Bact. Rev. *22*:99–142.

Jensen, K. A., Kirk, I., Kolmark, G., and Westergaard, M., 1951. Chemically induced mutations in *Neurospora*. Cold Spring Harbor Symposia Quant. Biol. *16*:245–261.

Kalckar, H. M., 1957a. Biochemical mutations in man and microorganisms. Science *125*:105–108.

Ibid., 1957b. Some considerations regarding biochemical genetics in man. Perspectives Biol. & Med. *1*:3–16.

Kalckar, H. M., Anderson, E. P., and Isselbacher, K. J., 1956. Galactosemia, a congenital defect in a nucleotide transferase. Biochim. et biophys. acta *20*:262–268.

Kanazir, D., 1958. The apparent mutagenicity of thymine deficiency. Biochim. et biophys. acta 30:20–23.

Kanazir, D., and Errera, M., 1956. Alterations of intracellular deoxyribonucleic acid and their biological consequence. Cold Spring Harbor Symposia Quant. Biol. 21:19–29.

Kaudewitz, F., 1959a. Production of bacterial mutants with nitrous acid. Nature 183:1829–1830.

Ibid., 1959b. Inaktivierende und mutagene Wirkung salpetrige Saure auf Zellen von Escherichia coli. Z. Naturforsch. 14b:528–537.

Kaudewitz, F. von, Vielmetter, W., and Friedrich-Freksa, H., 1958. Mutagene Wirkung des Zerfalles von radioaktiven Phosphor nach Einbau in Zellen von Escherichia coli. Z. Naturforsch. 13b:793–802.

Kelner, A., 1949. Photoreactivation of ultraviolet irradiated Escherichia coli with special reference to the dose reduction principle and to ultraviolet-induced mutation. J. Bact. 58:511–522.

King, J. T., and Briggs, R., 1955. Changes in the nuclei of differentiating gastrula cells as demonstrated by nuclear transplantation. Proc. Nat. Acad. Sci. U. S. 41:321–325.

Ibid., 1956. Serial transplantation of embryonic nuclei. Cold Spring Harbor Symposia Quant. Biol. 21:271–290.

Kirby-Smith, J. S., and Craig, D. L., 1957. The induction of chromosome aberrations in Tradescantia by ultraviolet radiation. Genetics 42:176–187.

Knox, W. E., 1958. Sir Archibald Garrod's "Inborn Errors of Metabolism" II. Alkaptonuria. Am. J. Human Genet. 10:95–124.

Knox, W. E., and Hsia, D. Y., 1957. Pathogenetic problems in phenylketonuria. Am. J. Med. 22:687–702.

Knox, W. E., and Messinger, E. C., 1958. The detection in the heterozygote of the metabolic effect of the recessive gene for phenylketonuria. Am. J. Human Genetics 10:53–60.

Koch, A. L., 1956. The metabolism of methylpurines by Escherichia coli. I. Tracer studies. J. Biol. Chem. 219:181–188.

Koch, A. L., and Lamont, W. A., 1956. The metabolism of methylpurines by Escherichia coli. II. Enzymatic studies. J. Biol. Chem. 219:189–201.

Kolmark, G., 1956. Mutagenic properties of certain esters of inorganic acids investigated by the Neurospora back mutation test. Compt. Rend. Trav. Lab. Carlsberg, Ser. Physiol. 26:205–220.

Kornberg, A., 1957. Pathways of Enzymatic Synthesis of Nucleotides and Polynucleotides in McElroy and Glass, Editors, The Chemical Basis of Heredity. Baltimore, Johns Hopkins Press.

Kramer, M., and Straub, F. B., 1957. Induced penicillinase formation in resting bacterial cells. III. Induction of penicillinase formation by extracts of Bacillus cereus NRRL-B-569/H cells without penicillin. Acta physio. acad. sci. hung. 11:139–144, (in English, Chem. Abstr. 51:18, 13992).

LaCour, L. F., and Pelc, S. R., 1958. Effect of colchicine on utilization of labeled thymidine during chromosomal reproduction. Nature 182:506–508.

Ibid., 1959. Effect of colchicine on the utilization of thymidine labeled with tritium during chromosomal reproduction. Nature 183:1455–56.

LaDu, B. N., Zannoni, V. G., Laster, L., and Seegmiller, J. E., 1958. Nature of the defect in tyrosine metabolism in alcaptonuria. J. Biol. Chem. 230:251–260.

Lawley, P. D., 1957. The relative reactivities of deoxyribonucleotides and of the bases of DNA towards alkylating agents. Biochim. et biophys. acta 26:450–451.

REFERENCES

Lawrence, H. S., 1959. Homograft sensitivity. Physiol. Rev. 39:811–859.

Lea, D. E., 1955. Actions of Radiations on Living Cells, ed. 2, London, Cambridge University Press.

Lea, D. E., and Catcheside, D. G., 1945. The bearing of radiation experiments on the size of the gene. J. Genet. 47:41–50.

Lederberg, J., 1947. Gene recombination and linked segregations in *Escherichia coli*. Genetics 32:505–525.

Ibid., 1955. Recombination mechanisms in bacteria. J. Cell. & Comp. Physiol. 45 sup. 2:75–107.

Lederberg, J., and Lederberg, Esther M., 1952. Replica plating and indirect selection of bacterial mutants. J. Bact. 63:399–406.

Lederberg, J., and Zinder, N., 1948. Concentration of biochemical mutants of bacteria with penicillin. J. Am. Chem. Soc. 70:4267.

Lehman, I. R., Zimmerman, S. B., Adler, J., Bessman, M. J., Simms, E. S., and Kornberg, A., 1958. Enzymatic synthesis of deoxyribonucleic acid. V. Chemical composition of the enzymatically synthesized deoxyribonucleic acid. Proc. Nat. Acad. Sci. U. S. 44:1191–1196.

Lerman, L. S., and Tolmach, L. J., 1957. Genetic transformation. I. Cellular incorporation of deoxyribonucleic acid (DNA) accompanying transformation in pneumococcus. Biochim. et biophys. acta 26:68–82.

Lester, H. E., and Gross, S. R., 1959. Efficient method for selection of auxotrophic mutants of Neurospora. Science 129:572.

Levan, A., 1951. Chemically induced chromosome reactions in *Allium cepa* and *Vicia faba*. Cold Spring Harbor Symposia Quant. Biol. 16:233–243.

Levinthal, C., 1956. The mechanism of DNA replication and genetic recombination in phage. Proc. Nat. Acad. Sci. U. S. 42:394–404.

Levinthal, C., and Crane, H. R., 1956. On the unwinding of DNA. Proc. Nat. Acad. Sci. U. S. 42:436–438.

Lewis, E. B., 1951. Pseudoallelism and gene evolution. Cold Spring Harbor Symposia Quant. Biol. 16:159–172.

Li, Ching-ts'ung, 1955. Population Genetics. Chicago, University of Chicago Press.

Lipman, F., 1958. Chairman's introduction: Some facts and problems (symposium on protein synthesis). Proc. Nat. Acad. Sci. U. S. 44:67–73.

Litman, R. M., and Pardee, A. B., 1956. Production of bacteriophage mutants by a disturbance of deoxyribonucleic acid metabolism. Nature 178:529–531.

Ibid., 1959. Mutations of bacteriophage T2 induced by bromouracil in the presence of chloramphenicol. Virology 8:125–127.

Logan, R., 1957. Incorporation of adenine labeled with carbon-14 into calf thymus nuclei in vitro. Biochim. et biophys. acta 26:227–228.

Loveless, A., 1959. The influence of radiomimetic substances on deoxyribonucleic acid synthesis and function studied in *Escherichia coli*/phage systems. III. Mutation of T2 bacteriophage as a consequence of alkylation *in vitro*: the uniqueness of ethylation. Proc. Roy. Soc. London s.B 150:497–508.

Luria, S. E., 1953. General Virology. New York, John Wiley and Sons Inc.

Luria, S. E., and Delbruck, M., 1943. Mutations of bacteria from virus sensitivity to virus resistance. Genetics 28:491–511.

Mandelstam, J., 1957. Turnover of protein in starved bacteria and its relation to the induced synthesis of enzyme. Nature 179:1179–81.

Mangelsdorf, P. C., 1958. The mutagenic effect of hybridizing maize and teosinte. Cold Spring Harbor Symposia Quant. Biol. 23:409–421.

Markert, C. L., and Moller, F., 1959. Multiple forms of enzymes: Tissue, ontogenetic and species specific patterns. Proc. Nat. Acad. Sci. U. S. *45*: 753–763.

Marmur, J., and Lane, D., 1960. Strand separation and specific recombination in deoxyribonucleic acids: Biological studies. Proc. Nat. Acad. Sci. U. S. *46*:453–461.

Mazia, D., 1952. Physiology of the Cell Nucleus *in* E. Barron, Editor, Modern Trends in Physiology and Biochemistry. New York, Academic Press, pp. 77–122.

McFall, E., Pardee, A. B., and Stent, G. S., 1958. Effects of radiophosphorous decay on some synthetic capacities of bacteria. Biochim. et biophys. acta *27*:282–297.

Medawar, P. B., 1958. The Croonian Lecture. The homograft reaction. Proc. Roy. Soc. London s.B *149*:145–166.

Merrill, J. P., 1959. Transplantation of normal tissues. Physiol. Rev. *39*:860–884.

Meselson, M., and Stahl, F. W., 1958. The replication of DNA in *Escherichia coli*. Proc. Nat. Acad. Sci. U. S. *44*:671–682.

Mitoma, C., 1956. Partially purified phenylalanine hydroxylase. Arch. Biochem. *60*:476–484.

Mitoma, C., Auld, R. M., and Udenfriend, S., 1957. Nature of the enzymic defect in phenylpyruvic oligophrenia. Proc. Soc. Exper. Biol. & Med. *94*:634–635.

Monod, J., 1956. Remarks on the Mechanism of Enzyme Induction *in* Gaebler, Editor, Enzymes: Units of Biological Structure and Function. New York, Academic Press, pp. 7–28.

Monod, J., and Cohn, M., 1952. La Biosynthese induite des enzymes (adaptation enzymatique). Advances Enzymol. *13*:67–119.

Morgan, Thomas Hunt, 1926. The Theory of the Gene. New Haven, Yale University Press.

Morton, R. K., 1958. Enzymic synthesis of coenzyme I in relation to chemical control of cell growth. Nature *181*:540–542.

Mountain, I. M., and Alexander, H. E., 1959. Infectivity of ribonucleic acid (RNA) from type I poliovirus in embryonated eggs. Proc. Soc. Exper. Biol. & Med. *101*:527–532.

Muller, H. J., 1927. Artificial transmutation of the gene. Science *66*:84–87.

Mundry, K. W., 1959. The effect of nitrous acid on Tobacco Mosaic Virus: Mutation not selection. Virology *9*:722–726.

Munier, R., and Cohen, G. N., 1956. Incorporation d'analogues structuraux d'aminoacides dans les protéines bactériennes. Biochim. et biophys. acta *21*:592–593.

Naora, H., Richter, G., and Naora, H., 1959. Further studies on the synthesis of RNA in enucleate *Acetabularia mediterranea*. Exper. Cell Res. *16*:434–436.

Neel, J. V., 1951. The inheritance of the sickling phenomenon with particular reference to sickle cell disease. Blood *6*:389–412.

Ibid., 1958. Genetic aspects of abnormal hemoglobins. Nat. Res. Council, Conference on Hemoglobin. J. Nat. Acad. Sci. Publ. 557, pp. 253–271.

Neidhardt, F. C., and Gros, F., 1957. Metabolic instability of the ribonucleic acid synthesized by *Escherichia coli* in the presence of chloromycetin. Biochim. et biophys. acta *25*:513–520.

Newcombe, H. B., 1949. Origin of bacterial variants. Nature *164*:150.

Newmeyer, D., and Tatum, E. L., 1953. Gene expression in Neurospora mutants requiring nicotinic acid or tryptophan. Am. J. Botany *40*:392–400.

Novick, A., 1956. Mutagens and antimutagens. Brookhaven Symposia Biol. 8:201–215.

Novick, A., and Szilard, L., 1951. Experiments on spontaneous and chemically induced mutations of bacteria growing in the chemostat. Cold Spring Harbor Symposia Quant. Biol. 16:337–343.

Ochoa, S., and Heppel, L., 1957. Polynucleotide Synthesis in McElroy and Glass, Editors, The Chemical Basis of Heredity. Baltimore, Johns Hopkins Press.

Osawa, S., Allfrey, V. G., and Mirsky, A. E., 1957. Mononucleotides of the cell nucleus. J. Gen. Physiol. 40:491–513.

Palade, G. E., and Siekevitz, P., 1956. Liver microsomes. An integrated morphological and biochemical study. J. Biophys. Biochem. Cytol. 2:171–201.

Pardee, A. B., 1959. The Control of Enzyme Activity in Boyer, Lardy and Myrback, Editors, The Enzymes, ed. 2. New York, Academic Press, Inc.

Pardee, A. B., Jacob, F., and Monod, J., 1959. The genetic control and cytoplasmic expression of "inducibility" in the synthesis of beta-galactosidase by E. coli. J. Mol. Biol. 1:165–178.

Pardee, A. B., and Prestidge, L. S., 1956. The dependence of nucleic acid synthesis on the presence of amino acids in Escherichia coli. J. Bacter. 71:677–683.

Pauling, L., 1954. Abnormality of hemoglobin molecules in hereditary hemolytic anemias. Harvey Lectures 49:216–241.

Pauling, L., Itano, H. A., Singer, S. J., and Wells, I. C., 1949. Sickle cell anemia, a molecular disease. Science 110:543–548.

Perutz, M. F., 1958. Some recent advances in molecular biology. Endeavour 17:190–203.

Pirie, N. W., 1937. The Meaninglessness of the Terms Life and Living in Needham and Green, Editors, Perspectives in Biochemistry. London, Cambridge University Press.

Plaut, W., and Mazia, D., 1956. The distribution of newly synthesized DNA in mitotic division. J. Biophys. Biochem. Cytol. 2:573–587.

Pollock, M. R., 1959. Induced Formation of Enzymes in Boyer, Lardy, and Myrback, Editors, The Enzymes, ed. 2. New York, Academic Press, Inc., pp. 619–680.

Pollock, M. R., and Kramer, M., 1958. Intermediates in the biosynthesis of bacterial penicillinase. Biochem. J. 70:665–681.

Pontecorvo, G., 1953. The genetics of Aspergillus nidulans. Advances Genet. 5:141–238.

Ibid., 1956. Allelism. Cold Spring Harbor Symposia Quant. Biol. 21:171–174.

Ibid., 1958. Trends in Genetic Analysis. New York, Columbia University Press.

Pontecorvo, G., and Roper, J., 1956. Resolving power of genetic analysis. Nature 178:83–84.

Ranney, H. M., Larson, D. L., and McCormack, G. H., Jr., 1953. Some clinical, biochemical and genetic observations on hemoglobin C. J. Clin. Invest. 32:1277–84.

Roman, H., and Jacob, F., 1958. A comparison of spontaneous and ultraviolet induced allelic recombination with reference to the recombination of outside markers. Cold Spring Harbor Symposia Quant. Biol. 23:155–160.

Rotman, B., and Spiegelman, S., 1954. On the origin of the carbon in the induced synthesis of beta-galactosidase in Escherichia coli. J. Bact. 68:419–429.

175

Russell, W. L., Russell, L. B., and Cupp, M. B., 1959. Dependence of mutation frequency on radiation dose rate in female mice. Proc. Nat. Acad. Sci. U. S. *45*:18–23.

Ryan, F. J., 1955. Spontaneous mutation in non-dividing bacteria. Genetics *40*:726–738.

Ibid., 1959. Bacterial mutation in a stationary phase and the question of cell turnover. J. Gen. Microbiol. *21*:530–549.

Sanger, F., and Thompson, E. O. P., 1953. Amino acid sequence in the glycyl chain of insulin. I. Identification of lower peptides from partial hydrolysates. II. Peptides from enzymic hydrolysates. Biochem. J. *53*:353–66, 366–74.

Schramm, G., 1958. Biochemistry of viruses. Ann. Rev. Biochem. 27:101–136.

Schwartz, D., 1954. Studies on the mechanism of crossing over. Genetics *39*: 692–700.

Schwartz, H., Spaet, T. H., Zuelzer, W. W., Neel, J. V., Robinson, A. R., and Kaufman, S. F., 1957. Combinations of hemoglobin G, hemoglobin S and thalassemia occurring in one family. Blood *12*:238–250.

Schwartz, N. M., and Strauss, B. S., 1958. Effect of tryptophan analogues on reversion of a tryptophan-requiring strain of *Escherichia coli*. Nature *182*: 888.

Schweet, R. S., Bovard, F., Allen, E., and Glassman, E., 1958a. The incorporation of amino acids into ribonucleic acid. Proc. Nat. Acad. Sci. U. S. *44*:173–177.

Schweet, R. S., Lamfrom, H., and Allen, E., 1958b. The synthesis of hemoglobin in a cell free system. Proc. Nat. Acad. Sci. U. S. *44*:1029–1035.

Sekiguchi, M., and Takagi, Y., 1959. Deoxyribonucleic acid synthesis of phage-infected *Escherichia coli* in the presence of Mitomycin C. Nature *183*:1134–35.

Sharon, N., and Lipman, F., 1957. Reactivity of analogs with pancreatic tryptophan activating enzyme. Arch. Biochem. 69:219–227.

Shiba, S., Terawaki, A., Taguchi, T., and Kawamata, J., 1959. Selective inhibition of formation of deoxyribonucleic acid in *Escherichia coli* by Mitomycin C. Nature *183*:1056–57.

Silver, W. S., and McElroy, W. D., 1954. Enzyme studies on nitrate and nitrite mutants of Neurospora. Arch. Biochem. *51*:379–94.

Simkin, J. L., 1959. Protein biosynthesis. Ann. Rev. Biochem. 28:145–170.

Simkin, J. L., and Work, T. S., 1957. Protein synthesis in guinea-pig liver. Incorporation of radioactive amino acids into proteins of the microsome fraction *in vivo*. Biochem. J. *65*:307–311.

Simpson, M. V., and Velick, S. F., 1954. The synthesis of aldolase and glyceraldehyde-3-phosphate dehydrogenase in the rabbit. J. Biol. Chem. *208*:61–71.

Sinsheimer, R. L., 1954. Nucleotides from T2r$^+$ bacteriophage. Science *120*: 551–553.

Ibid., 1959. A single-stranded deoxyribonucleic acid from bacteriophage ϕX 174. J. Mol. Biol. *1*:43–53.

Smith, K. C., Cordes, E., and Schweet, R. S., 1959. Fractionation of transfer ribonucleic acid. Biochim. et biophys. acta 33:286–7.

Snell, G. D., Smith, P. M., and Gabrielson, F., 1953. Analysis of the histocompatibility-2 locus in the mouse. J. Nat. Cancer Inst. *14*:457–480.

Spiegelman, S., 1957. Nucleic Acids and the Synthesis of Proteins *in* McElroy and Glass, Editors, The Chemical Basis of Heredity. Baltimore, Johns Hopkins Press.

REFERENCES

Spiegelman, S., Halvorson, H. O., and Ben-Ishai, R., 1955. Free Amino Acids and the Enzyme-Forming Mechanism *in* McElroy and Glass, Editors, Symposium on Amino Acid Metabolism. Baltimore, Johns Hopkins Press.

Spirin, A. S., Belozersii, A. N., Shugaeva, N. V., and Vanyushin, B. F., 1957. Species specificity of bacterial nucleic acids. Biokhimiya 22:744–53 (Chem. Abstr. 52 #7 5536i).

Spizizen, J., 1958. Transformation of biochemically deficient strains of *Bacillus subtilis* by deoxyribonucleate. Proc. Nat. Acad. Sci. U. S. 44:1072–78.

Sprunt, K., Redman, W. M., and Alexander, H. E., 1959. Infectious ribonucleic acid derived from enteroviruses. Proc. Soc. Exper. Biol. & Med., 101: 604–608.

Srb, A., and Owen, R., 1952. General Genetics. San Francisco, W. H. Freeman & Co.

Stacey, K. A., Cobb, M., Cousens, S. F., and Alexander, P., 1958. The reactions of the "radiomimetic" alkylating agents with macromolecules *in vitro*. Ann. New York Acad. Sc. 68:682–701.

Stadler, Joan, and Yanofsky, C., 1959. Studies on a series of tryptophan-independent strains derived from a tryptophan requiring mutant of *Escherichia coli*. Genetics 44:105–123.

Stadler, L. J., 1928. Mutations in barley induced by x-rays and radium. Science 68:186.

Ibid., 1954. The gene. Science 120:811–819.

Stanley, W. M., 1935. Isolation of a crystalline protein possessing the properties of tobacco mosaic virus. Science 81:644–645.

Steffensen, D., 1957. Effects of various cation imbalances on the frequency of x-ray-induced chromosomal aberrations in Tradescantia. Genetics 42:239–252.

Steinberg, D., and Anfinson, C. B., 1952. Evidence for intermediates in ovalbumin synthesis. J. Biol. Chem. 199:25–42.

Steinberg, D., and Mihalyi, E., 1957. The chemistry of proteins. Ann. Rev. Biochem. 26:373–418.

Steinberg, D., Vaughan, M., and Anfinson, C., 1956. Kinetic aspect of assembly and degradation of protein. Science 124:389–395.

Steinberg, R. A., and Thom, C., 1940. Chemical induction of genetic changes in Aspergilli. J. Hered. 31:61–63.

Stent, G. S., 1955. Decay of incorporated radioactive phosphorus during reproduction of bacteriophage T2. J. Gen. Physiol. 38:853–865.

Ibid., 1958. Mating in the reproduction of bacterial viruses. Advances Virus Res. 5:95–149.

Stent, Gunther S., Sato, Gordon H., and Jerne, N. K., 1959. Dispersal of the parental nucleic acid of bacteriophage T4 among its progeny. J. Mol. Biol. 1:134–146.

Stern, C., 1954. Two or three bristles. Am. Scientist 42:213–247.

Stevens, C. M., and Mylroie, A., 1953. Inhibition effects in back-mutation tests with mutants of Neurospora. Nature 171:179–180.

Stone, W. S., Wyss, O., and Haas, F., 1947. The production of mutations in *Staphylococcus aureus* by irradiation of the substrate. Proc. Nat. Acad. Sci. U. S. 33:59–66.

Strauss, B. S., 1955. A mechanism of gene interaction. Am. Naturalist 89: 141–150.

Ibid., 1956. The nature of the lesion in the succinate-requiring mutants of *Neurospora crassa*: Interaction between carbohydrate and nitrogen metabolism. J. Gen. Microbiol. 14:494–511.

Ibid., 1958. The genetic effect of incorporated radioisotopes: The transmutation problem. Radiation Research 8:234–247.

Ibid., 1959. The effect of the distribution of sulfur on the lethal action of incorporated $S^{35}O_4$. Radiation Research 11:345–356.

Strauss, B. S., and Minagawa, T., 1959. The formation of methionine by a methionine-requiring mutant. J. Gen. Microbiol. 20:237–245.

Strauss, B. S., and Pierog, S., 1954. Gene interactions: The mode of action of the suppressor of acetate-requiring mutants of *Neurospora crassa*. J. Gen. Microbiol. 10:221–235.

Strauss, B., and Okubo, S., 1960. Protein synthesis and the induction of mutations in *Escherichia coli* by alkylating agents. J. Bact. 79:464–473.

Sueoka, Noboru, 1960. Mitotic replication of deoxyribonucleic acid in *Chlamydomonas reinhardi*. Proc. Nat. Acad. Sci. U. S. 46:83–90.

Suskind, S. R., 1957. Properties of a protein antigenically related to tryptophan synthetase in *Neurospora crassa*. J. Bact. 74:308–318.

Suskind, S. R., and Kurek, Loretta I., 1959. On a mechanism of suppressor gene regulation of tryptophan synthetase activity in *Neurospora crassa*. Proc. Nat. Acad. Sci. U. S. 45:193–196.

Suter, C. M., 1944. The Organic Chemistry of Sulfur, New York, John Wiley & Sons.

Swick, R. W., Koch, A. L., and Handa, D. T., 1956. The measurement of nucleic acid turnover in rat liver. Arch. Biochem. 63:226–242.

Takahara, S., Sato, H., Doi, M., and Mihara, S., 1952. Acatalasemia. III. On the heredity of Acatalasemia. Proc. Japan. Acad. 28:585–588.

Taylor, J. H., 1957. The time and mode of duplication of chromosomes. Am. Naturalist 91:209–221.

Ibid., 1958. The organization and duplication of genetic material. Proc. Intern. Cong. Genet., 10th congr., Toronto 1:63–78.

Taylor, J. H., Wood, P. S., and Hughes, W. L., 1957. The organization and duplication of chromosomes as revealed by autoradiographic studies using tritium-labeled thymidine. Proc. Nat. Acad. Sci. U. S. 43:122–128.

Tessman, I., 1959. Some unusual properties of the nucleic acid in bacteriophages S13 and ϕX174. Virology 7:263–275.

Thom, C., and Steinberg, R. A., 1939. Chemical inductions of genetic changes in fungi. Proc. Nat. Acad. Sci. U. S. 25:329–335.

Thomas, C. A., Jr., 1959. The release and stability of the large subunit of DNA from T2 and T4 bacteriophage. J. Gen. Physiol. 42:503–523.

Tsugita, A., and Fraenkel-Conrat, H., 1960. The amino acid composition and C-terminal sequence of a chemically evoked mutant of TMV. Proc. Nat. Acad. Sci. U. S. 46:636–642.

Udenfriend, S., and Bessman, S. P., 1953. The hydroxylation of phenylalanine and antipyrine in phenylpyruvic oligophrenia. J. Biol. Chem. 203:961–966.

van Bekkum, D. W., and Vos, O., 1957. Immunological aspects of homo- and heterologous bone marrow transplantation in irradiated animals. J. Cell. & Comp. Physiol. 50 suppl. 1: 139–156.

Vendrely, R., 1955. The Deoxyribonucleic Acid Content of the Nucleus *in* Chargaff and Davidson, Editors, The Nucleic Acids, Vol. 2. New York, Academic Press.

Visconti, N., and Delbruck, M., 1953. The mechanism of genetic recombination in phage. Genetics 38:5–33.

Volkin, E., Astrachan, L., and Countryman, J. L., 1958. Metabolism of RNA phosphorus in *Escherichia coli* infected with bacteriophage T7. Virology 6:545–555.

Wagner, R. P., and Mitchell, H. K., 1955. Genetics and Metabolism. New York, John Wiley & Sons, Inc.

Wallace, H. W., Moldave, K., and Meister, A., 1957. Conversion of phenylalanine to tyrosine in phenylpyruvic oligophrenia. Proc. Soc. Exper. Biol. & Med. 94:632–633.

Watanabe, I., Kiho, Y., and Miura, K., 1958. Effect of chloramphenicol on ribonucleic acid metabolism in *E. coli* infected with T2 phage. Nature *181:* 1127.

Watson, J. D., and Crick, F. H. C., 1953a. Molecular structure of nucleic acids. Nature *171:*737–738.

Ibid., 1953b. Genetical implications of the structure of deoxyribose nucleic acid. Nature *171:*964–967.

Ibid., 1953c. The structure of DNA. Cold Spring Harbor Symposia Quant. Biol. *18:*123–131.

Westergaard, M., 1957a. Chemical mutagenesis in relation to the concept of the gene. Experientia *13:*224–234.

Ibid., 1957b. On the Identification of Genetic and Non-genetic Variation in Bacteria *in* Wolstenholme and O'Conner, Editors, Drug Resistance in Micro-Organisms. Ciba Foundation Symposia, pp. 280–293.

Wiener, A. S., and Wexler, I. B., 1958. Heredity of the Blood Groups. New York, Grune and Stratton.

Williams, R. J., 1951. Introduction, general discussion and tentative conclusions in Biochemical Institute Studies IV. Individual metabolic patterns and human disease: an exploratory study utilizing predominantly paper chromatographic methods. Univ. Texas Publ. *5109:*7–21.

Ibid., 1956. Biochemical Individuality. The Basis for the Genetotrophic Concept. New York, John Wiley and Sons.

Witkin, Evelyn M., 1951. Nuclear segregation and the delayed appearance of induced mutants in *Escherichia coli.* Cold Spring Harbor Symposia Quant. Biol. *16:*357–372.

Ibid., 1956. Time, temperature and protein synthesis: A study of ultraviolet induced mutation in bacteria. Cold Spring Harbor Symposia Quant. Biol. *21:*123–140.

Ibid., 1959. Post-irradiation metabolism and the timing of ultraviolet-induced mutations in bacteria. Proc. Intern. Congr. Genet., 10th Congr., Toronto *1:*280–299.

Wolff, S., and Luippold, H. E., 1955. Metabolism and chromosome-break rejoining. Science *122:*231–232.

Woodward, D. O., Partridge, C. W. H., and Giles, N. H., 1958. Complementation at the ad-4 locus in *Neurospora crassa.* Proc. Nat. Acad. Sci. U. S. *44:*1237–44.

Woodward, V. W., DeZeeuw, J. R., and Srb, A. M., 1954. The separation and isolation of particular biochemical mutants of Neurospora by differential germination of conidia followed by filtration and selective plating. Proc. Nat. Acad. Sci. U. S. *40:*192–200.

Yanofsky, C., 1956. Gene interactions in Enzyme Synthesis *in* Gaebler, Editor, Enzymes: Units of Biological Structure and Function. New York, Academic Press.

Ibid., 1959. A second reaction catalyzed by the tryptophan synthetase of *Escherichia coli.* Biochim. et biophys. acta *31:*408–416.

Yanofsky, C., and Bonner, D. M., 1955. Gene interaction in tryptophan synthetase formation. Genetics *40:*761–769.

REFERENCES

Yates, R. A., and Pardee, A. B., 1957. Control by uracil of formation of enzymes required for orotate synthesis. J. Biol. Chem. 227:677–692.

Ycas, M., 1958. The Protein Text *in* Symposium on Information Theory in Biology. New York, Pergamon Press, 70–102.

Ycas, M., and Vincent, W., 1960. A ribonucleic acid fraction from yeast related in composition to desoxyribonucleic acid. Proc. Nat. Acad. Sci. U. S. 46:804–811.

Zalokar, M., 1958. Primary gene product: Protein or RNA? Proc. Intern. Congr. Genet., 10th congr., Toronto 2:330.

Ibid., 1959. Nuclear origin of ribonucleic acid. Nature 183:1330.

Zamecnik, P. C., Keller, E. B., Littlefield, J. W., Hoagland, M. B., and Loftfield, R. B., 1956. Mechanism of incorporation of labeled amino acids into protein. J. Cell. & Comp. Physiol. 47 suppl. 1: 81–101.

Zamecnik, P., Stephenson, M. L., and Hecht, L., 1958. Intermediate reactions in amino acid incorporation. Proc. Nat. Acad. Sci. U. S. 44:73–78.

Zamenhof, S., 1957. Properties of the Transforming Principles *in* McElroy and Glass, Editors, The Chemical Basis of Heredity. Baltimore, Johns Hopkins Press.

Zamenhof, S., deGiovanni, R., and Greer, S., 1957. Induced and spontaneous gene unstabilization. Genetics 42:403–404.

Author Index

182

Subject Index

187

Date Due

11/24/61			
OCT 1 2 '62			
OCT 26 62			
DEC 10 '62			
JAN 3 '63			
MAY 1 0 '66			
FEB 2 8 1974			
OCT 1 0 1977			
MAY 1 1979			
APR 2 0 1982			
JUL 1 5 1982			
APR 1 4 1992			
APR 0 2 1994			
PRINTED IN U. S. A.